W9-BPM-990

GOING PLACES

STEPHEN GAMMELL

Stephen Gammell taught himself to draw. As a second grader, he drew all the time. He learned about illustrations by looking at them in many magazines and books.

"I make it up as I go along," says Stephen Gammell about his drawing. This is also his advice to young artists. He says, "If you don't know what something looks like, make it up!" Certainly the flying machine that Stephen Gammell made up for the cover is one of a kind.

Acknowledgments appear on page 192, which constitutes an extension of this copyright page.

ISBN 0–663–54654–0

4 5 6 7 8 9 10 VHP 98 97 96 95 94

New Dimensions

IN THE

WORLD OF READING

GOING PLACES

PROGRAM AUTHORS

James F. Baumann
Theodore Clymer
Carl Grant
Elfrieda H. Hiebert
Roselmina Indrisano
Dale D. Johnson
Connie Juel
Jeanne R. Paratore
P. David Pearson
Taffy E. Raphael
Marian Davies Toth
Richard L. Venezky

SILVER BURDETT GINN

NEEDHAM, MA MORRISTOWN, NJ

ATLANTA, GA DALLAS, TX DEERFIELD, IL MENLO PARK, CA

Unit 1 Theme

BEST FOOT FORWARD

Unit 2 Theme

Near and Far

BEST FOOT FORWARD

What does it mean to put your best foot forward?

When do you put your best foot forward?

Unit 1 Theme

THE MARY MCLEOD BETHUNE MEMORIAL, Washington, D.C., *bronze statue by Robert Berks, American, c. 1974*

Theme Books for

Best Foot Forward

Sometimes working alone isn't enough to do a job. That's when you need teamwork!

Who let the classroom pets out of their cages? And who allowed the toads to escape? Watch Ernie try to solve this mystery in ***The 123 Zoo Mystery*** by Susan Pearson. To find *all* the answers, Ernie needs her friends to help.

❧ Paddy Pig doesn't care if his poems are a bit unusual. No matter what his friends say, he doesn't stop writing. If you like riddles and poems that rhyme, you'll have fun reading ***Paddy Pig's Poems*** by Donald Charles.

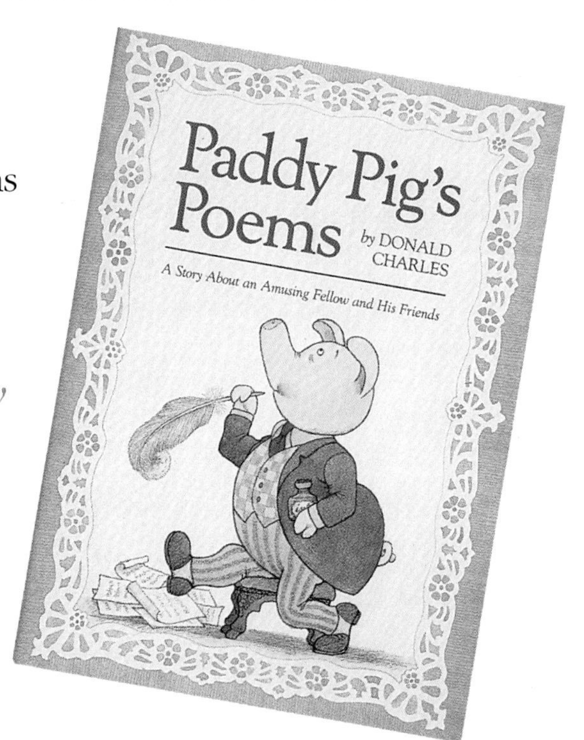

More Books to Enjoy

The Big Balloon Race by Eleanor Coerr
Martin's Hats by Joan Blos
Gila Monsters Meet You at the Airport by Marjorie Weinman Sharmat
Old Turtle's Winter Games by Leonard Kessler

WATCH OUT, RONALD MORGAN!

written by Patricia Reilly Giff
illustrated by Susanna Natti

It all started when the bell rang. I raced across the school yard and slid over a patch of ice.

"Watch out!" Rosemary yelled. But it was too late. I bumped into her and she landed in a snow pile.

After I hung up my jacket, I fed the goldfish. I fed Frank, the gerbil, too.

"Oh, no," Rosemary said. "You fed the gerbil food to Goldie."

"Oh," I said. "The boxes look the same."

Billy shook his head. "Can't you read the letters? F is for fish. G is for gerbil."

"Don't worry," said Michael, my best friend. He poured more water into the fish tank.

At recess Miss Tyler wouldn't let us go outside. "You'll get snow in your sneakers," she said. So we played kickball in the gym. The ball bounced off my head.

Marc said, "I'm glad you're not on my team."

And Rosemary said, "Can't you even see the ball?"

Then it was time for book reports. "Who'd like to be first?" Miss Tyler asked. I ducked behind my desk.

"Ronald Morgan," said Miss Tyler.

"My book is *Lennie Lion*," I said. I held up my report and blinked to see the words. "This book is about a lion named Lennie. He's ferocious and good."

"Great," said Jan.

"Grr," said Michael.

"Lovely," said Miss Tyler.

After lunch we looked out the window. Everything was white.

"It's time for a winter classroom," said Miss Tyler. I bent over my desk and drew a snowflake. Then I cut it out.

Tom said, "Ronald Morgan, that's a wiggly snowflake. Why don't you cut on the lines?"

And Rosemary said, "I think your snowflake is melting."

When it was time to go home, Miss Tyler gave me a note for my mother and father. "Maybe you need glasses," she said.

At lunch the next day, Marc asked, "When do you get your glasses?"

I took a bite of my peanut butter sandwich. "I go to the doctor today."

And Michael asked, "Can I go with you?"

In the shopping mall we passed my father's tie store. I waved to him and he waved back. In Doctor Sims's window was a huge pair of eyeglasses. Michael and I made believe they belonged to a monster.

"Look at these Es," said Doctor Sims. "Which way do they point?"

I squinted my eyes and pointed. The Es looked smaller and smaller.

Then Doctor Sims said, "It's hard for you to see them."

And my mother said, "You'll look great in glasses."

"Yes," said the doctor. "Glasses will help. They'll make everything look sharp and clear."

Next we went to the counter. I tried on a pair of red frames. They slid down over my nose. I tried round ones and square ones. Then I put on blue frames and looked in the mirror.

"Good," said my mother.

"Good," said Michael.

And Doctor Sims said, "The lenses will be ready in an hour."

We went to the tie store. "My glasses are great," I told my father.

He smiled. "Now everything will look the way it should," he said.

Then my glasses were ready.

"Just wait till tomorrow," I said. "I'll be the best ballplayer, the best reader, the best speller, the best everything."

"Wow," said Michael.

"Nice," said my mother.

"Yes," I told them. "I'll be the superkid of the school."

Before school, I threw some snowballs. "You missed!" Jimmy yelled, and threw one at me. It landed right on my nose.

Rosemary laughed. "Your glasses need windshield wipers," she said.

But Michael looked worried. "How come your glasses don't work?"

In the classroom, I hung up my jacket and put my hat on the shelf.

"Where is our fish monitor?" asked Miss Tyler.

I ran to give Goldie some food. This time I looked at the box. The letters looked big and sharp. "G is for Goldie," I said. "F is for Frank."

"Oh, no," said Billy. "F is for fish. G is for gerbil."

And Michael frowned. "I don't think your glasses help."

I tiptoed into the closet and put the glasses inside my hat.

Alice looked at me. “Where are your blue glasses?” she whispered.

I shook my head. “I have terrible glasses. I’ll never be the superkid of the class.”

When it was time to go home, Miss Tyler gave me another note. My mother helped me with some of the words.

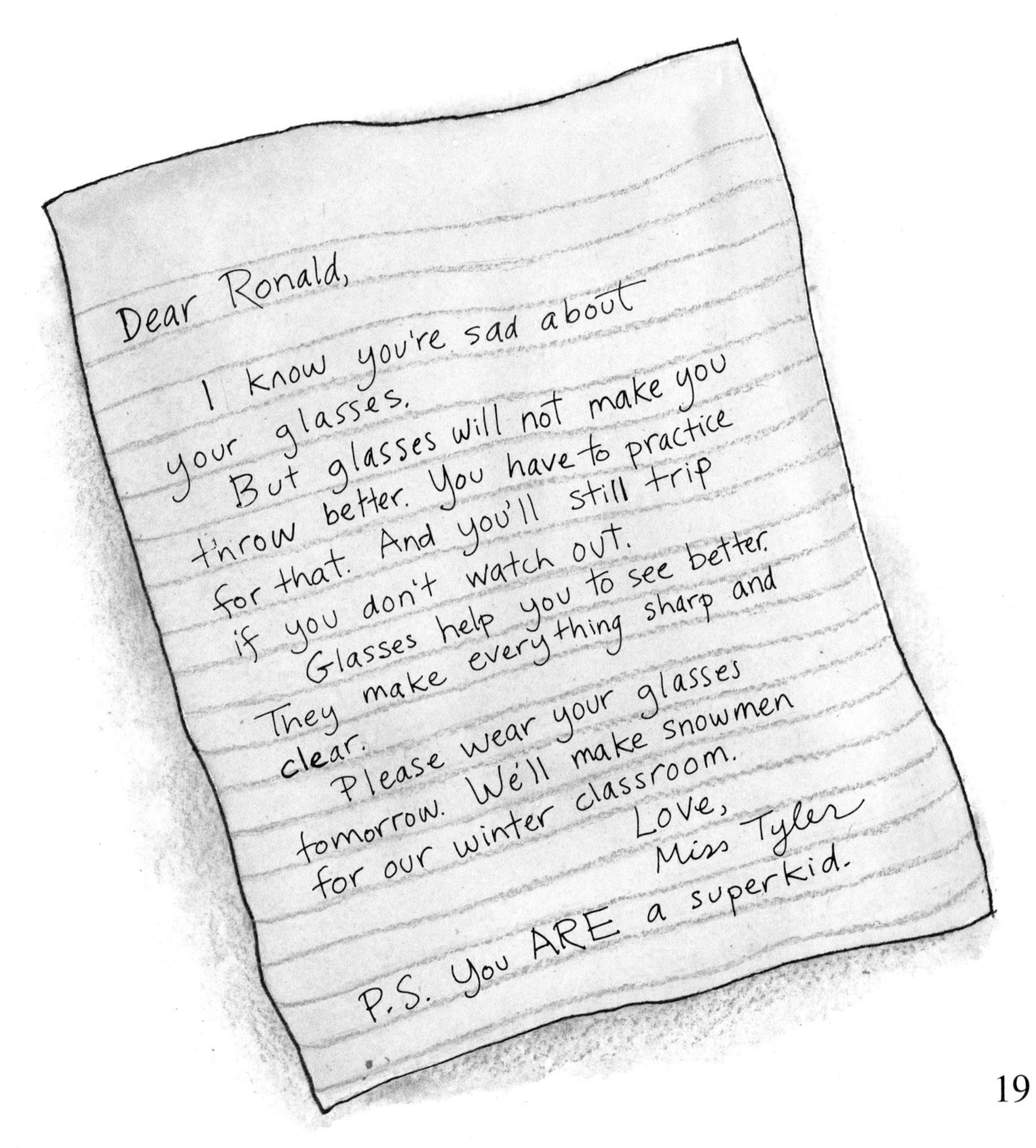

Dear Ronald,

I know you're sad about your glasses.

But glasses will not make you throw better. You have to practice for that. And you'll still trip if you don't watch out.

Glasses help you to see better. They make everything sharp and clear.

Please wear your glasses tomorrow. We'll make snowmen for our winter classroom.

Love,
Miss Tyler

P.S. You ARE a superkid.

In school I drew a snowman and picked up the scissors to cut.

"Hey," I said, "Miss Tyler's right. The lines are sharp and clear."

"Good snowman," said Rosemary.

And Miss Tyler said, "Just what we need for our winter classroom."

I picked up my blue crayon and drew a few more lines. "Now he's a super snowman," I said.

We all cheered.

Reader's Response ~ What do you think a superkid is? Would you want to be one? Tell why or why not.

FANTASTIC EYES

Here are some interesting facts about eyes—your eyes and those of a few other creatures.

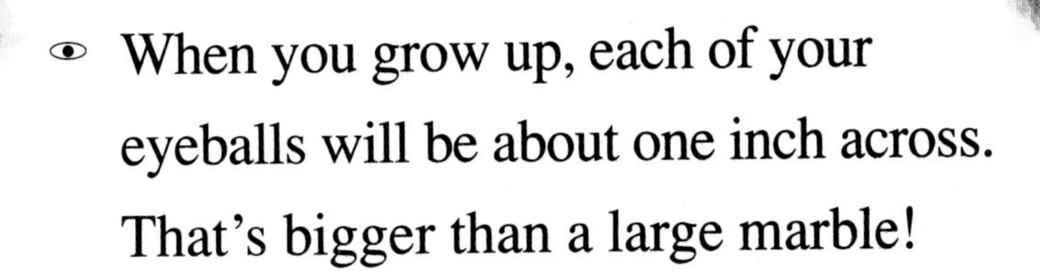

- When you grow up, each of your eyeballs will be about one inch across. That's bigger than a large marble!

- It takes six muscles to move each of your eyes. And they do a lot of work you don't even think about.

- Your eyes can see about 200 different colors. Do you know the names of that many colors?

- Cats' pupils can open wider than ours, and they have a special layer inside their eyes, so they see better at night.

- A dragonfly has up to 30,000 separate "eyes." Imagine that!

Music, Music For Everyone

♪ ♬ ♪

by
Vera B. Williams

Our big chair often sits in our living room empty now.

When I first got my accordion, Grandma and Mama used to sit in that chair together to listen to me practice. And every day after school while Mama was at her job at the diner, Grandma would be sitting in the chair by the window. Even if it was snowing big flakes down on her hair, she would lean way out to call, "Hurry up, Pussycat. I've got something nice for you."

But now Grandma is sick. She has to stay upstairs in the big bed in Aunt Ida and Uncle Sandy's extra room. Mama and Aunt Ida and Uncle Sandy and I take turns taking care of her. When I come home from school, I run right upstairs to ask Grandma if she wants anything. I carry up the soup Mama has left for her. I water her plants and report if the Christmas cactus has any flowers yet. Then I sit on her bed and tell her about everything.

Grandma likes it when my friends Leora, Jenny, and Mae come home with me because we play music for her. Leora plays the drums. Mae plays the flute. Jenny plays fiddle and I play my accordion. One time we played a dance for Grandma that we learned in the music club at school.

Grandma clapped until it made her too tired. She told us it was like the music in the village where she lived when she was a girl. It made her want to dance right down the street. We had to keep her from trying to hop out of bed to go to the kitchen to fix us a treat.

Leora and Jenny and Mae and I left Grandma to rest and went down to get our own treat. We squeezed together into our big chair to eat it.

"It feels sad down here without your grandma," Leora said. "Even your big money jar up there looks sad and empty."

"Remember how it was full to the top and I couldn't even lift it when we bought the chair for my mother?" I said.

"And remember how it was more than half full when you got your accordion?" Jenny said.

"I bet it's empty now because your mother has to spend all her money to take care of your grandma till she gets better. That's how it was when my father had his accident and couldn't go to work for a long time," Mae said.

Mae had a dime in her pocket and she dropped it into the jar. "That will make it look a little fuller anyway," she said as she went home.

But after Jenny and Leora and Mae went home, our jar looked even emptier to me. I wondered how we would ever be able to fill it up again while Grandma was sick. I wondered when Grandma would be able to come downstairs again. Even our beautiful chair with roses all over it seemed empty with just me in the corner of it. The whole house seemed so empty and so quiet.

I got out my accordion and I started to play. The notes sounded beautiful in the empty room. One song that is an old tune sounded so pretty I played it over and over. I remembered what my mother had told me about my other grandma and how she used to play the accordion. Even when she was a girl not much bigger than I, she would get up and play at a party or a wedding so the company could dance and sing. Then people would stamp their feet and yell, "More, more!" When they went home, they would leave money on the table for her.

That's how I got my idea for how I could help fill up the jar again. I ran right upstairs. "Grandma," I whispered. "Grandma?"

"Is that you, Pussycat?" she answered in a sleepy voice. "I was just having such a nice dream about you. Then I woke up and heard you playing that beautiful old song. Come. Sit here and brush my hair."

I brushed Grandma's hair and told her my whole idea. She thought it was a great idea. "But tell the truth, Grandma," I begged her. "Do you think kids could really do that?"

"I think you and Jenny and Leora and Mae could do it. No question. No question at all," she answered. "Only don't wait a minute to talk to them about it. Go call and ask them now."

And that was how the Oak Street Band got started.

Our music teachers helped us pick out pieces we could all play together. Aunt Ida, who plays guitar, helped us practice. We practiced on our back porch. One day our neighbor leaned out his window in his pajamas and yelled, “Listen, kids, you sound great but give me a break. I work at night. I’ve got to get some sleep in the daytime.” After that we practiced inside. Grandma said it was helping her get better faster than anything.

At last my accordion teacher said we sounded very good. Uncle Sandy said so too. Aunt Ida and Grandma said we were terrific. Mama said she thought anyone would be glad to have us play for them.

It was Leora's mother who gave us our first job. She asked us to come and play at a party for Leora's great-grandmother and great-grandfather. It was going to be a special anniversary for them. It was fifty years ago on that day they first opened their market on our corner. Now Leora's mother takes care of the market. She always plays the radio loud while she works. But for the party she said there just had to be live music.

All of Leora's aunts and uncles and cousins came to the party. Lots of people from our block came too. Mama and Aunt Ida and Uncle Sandy walked down from our house very slowly with Grandma. It was Grandma's first big day out.

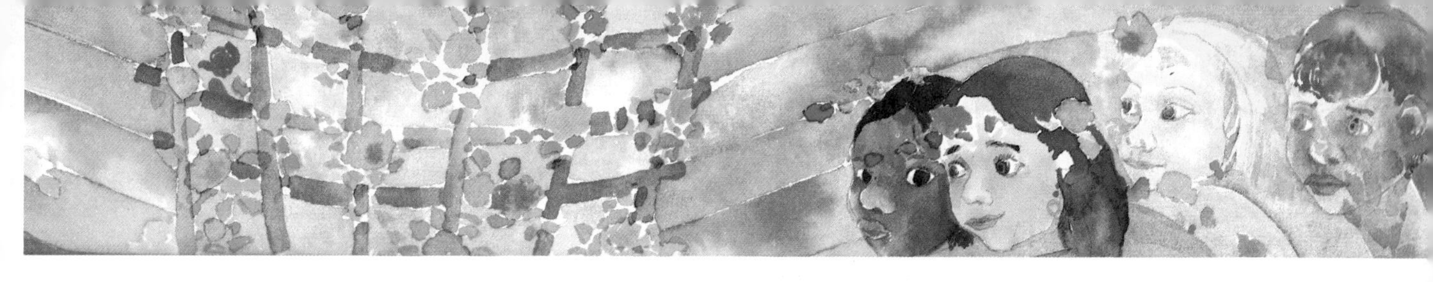

There was a long table in the backyard made from little tables all pushed together. It was covered with so many big dishes of food you could hardly see the tablecloth. But I was too excited to eat anything.

Leora and Jenny and Mae and I waited over by the rosebush. Each of us had her instrument all ready. But everyone else went on eating and talking and eating some more. We didn't see how they would ever get around to listening to us. And we didn't see how we could be brave enough to begin.

At last Leora's mother pulled us right up in front of everybody. She banged on a pitcher with a spoon to get attention.

Then she introduced each one of us. "And *now* we're going to have music," she said. "Music and dancing for everyone."

It was quiet as school assembly. Every single person there was looking right at Leora and Jenny and Mae and me. But we just stood there and stared right back. Then I heard my grandma whisper, "Play, Pussycat. Play anything. Just like you used to play for me."

I put my fingers on the keys and buttons of my accordion. Jenny tucked her fiddle under her chin. Mae put her flute to her mouth. Leora held up her drums. After that we played and played. We made mistakes, but we played like a real band. The little lanterns came on. Everyone danced.

Mama and Aunt Ida and Uncle Sandy smiled at us every time they danced by. Grandma kept time nodding her head and tapping with the cane she uses now. Leora and Jenny and Mae and I forgot about being scared. We loved the sound of the Oak Street Band.

And afterward everybody clapped and shouted. Leora's great-grandfather and great-grandmother thanked us. They said we had made their party something they would always remember. Leora's father piled up plates of food for us. My mama arranged for Leora, Jenny, and Mae to stay over at our house. And when we finally all went out the gate together, late at night, Leora's mother tucked an envelope with our money into Leora's pocket.

As soon as we got home, we piled into my bed to divide the money. We made four equal shares. Leora said she was going to save up for a bigger drum. Mae wasn't sure what she would do with her share. Jenny fell asleep before she could tell us. But I couldn't even lie down until I climbed up and put mine right into our big jar on the shelf near our chair.

Reader's Response ~ What would you enjoy doing as part of a team?

Dear Readers,

I'm glad you've been able to read my story *Music, Music for Everyone*, reprinted here just the way I wrote it. You can find my book with more pictures of Rosa and her family and friends on your library shelf. There you will also find the two other books about Rosa displayed on this page.

The ideas for these stories came from my own childhood. I grew up in a neighborhood where people looked out for one another. My mother often helped our neighbors. I have strong and lively memories of that time, which I have shown in the bright colors and shades of my pictures.

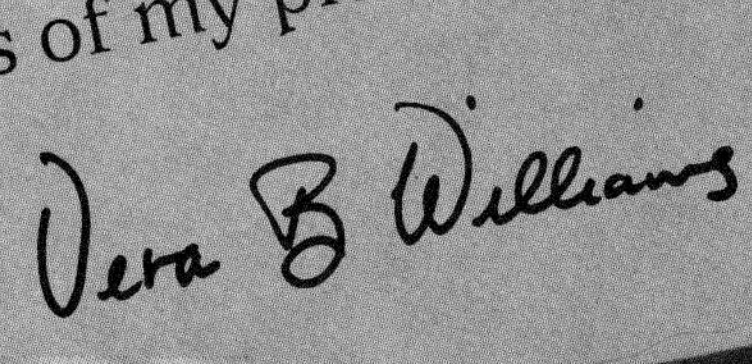

BOOKS
15
6
7

My shelf of books! I love them so!
They take me where I want to go.

Adventure, deeds of every age
Lie captured on the printed page;
Through them I hear the swish of seas,
The wind in lofty mountain trees.
Their magic brings before my gaze
Heroes of stirring, ancient days.
Here in my chair, through day or night,
They lend me wings for daring flight.

I love my shelf of books, they are
Pathways to sun . . . and moon . . . and star!

Katherine Edelman

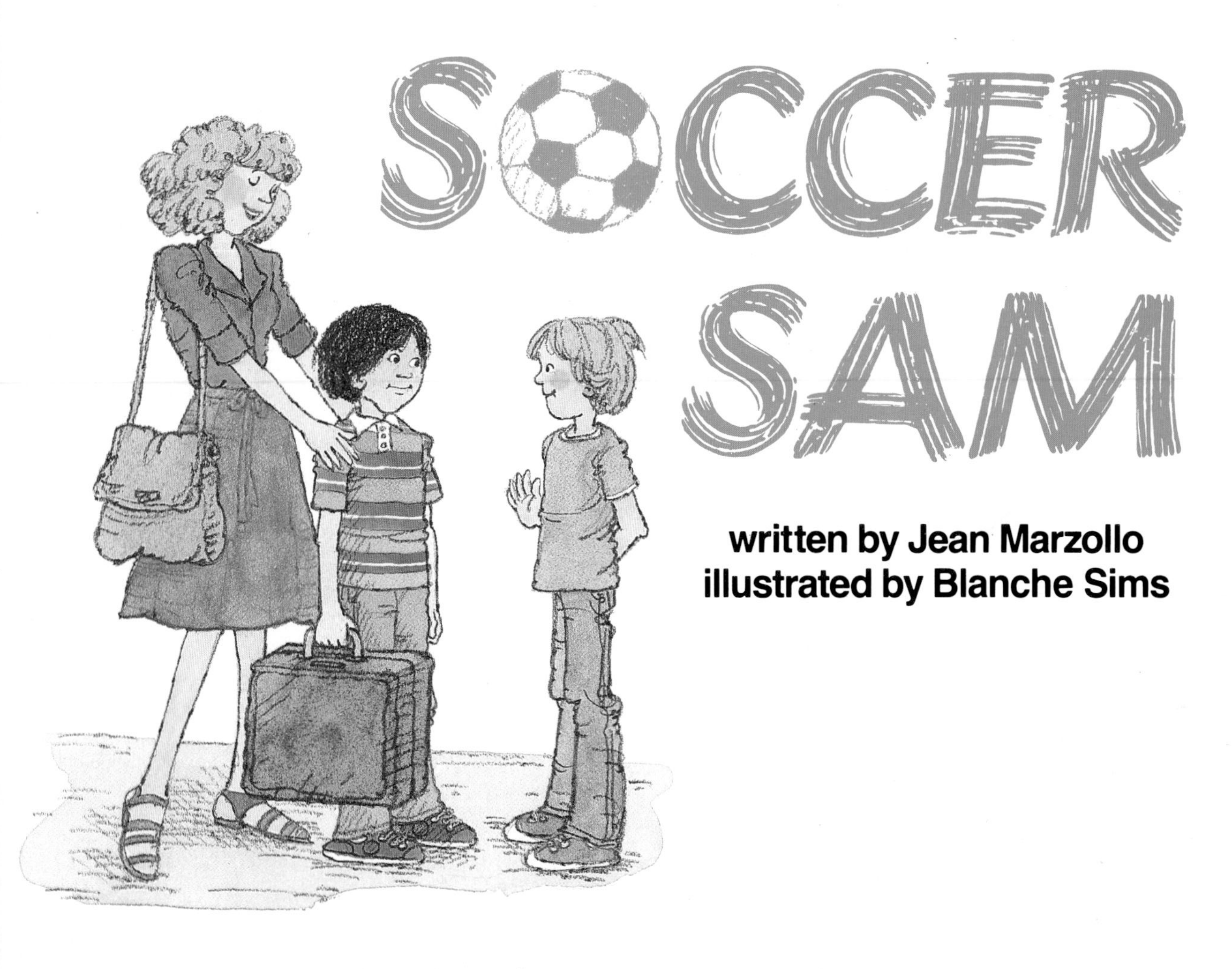

SOCCER SAM

written by Jean Marzollo
illustrated by Blanche Sims

The plane from Mexico was landing. Sam stood at the airport window and watched. He was going to meet his cousin Marco for the first time.

Soon a boy Sam's size came through the door. Sam's mother hugged him. "Marco, this is Sam," she said slowly. "Sam, this is Marco."

"Hi," said Sam. Suddenly he felt shy.

"¡Hola!" said Marco softly.

In the car Marco was very quiet. So was Sam.

"We are happy you have come to live with us for a year," said Sam's mother.

"Sí," said Marco. But he didn't look happy. He just looked out the window.

"You like sports?" asked Sam. Sam loved sports. He was very good at them too.

Marco shrugged.

"He doesn't speak much English," said Sam's mother. When they got home, she said, "Take Marco out to play, Sam. Introduce him to your friends."

"What if he doesn't understand what we say?" asked Sam.

"Speak slowly," said his mom. "He'll learn."

Sam and Marco went outside. At the end of the street, kids were shooting baskets. Sam's friend Rosie tossed him the ball. Sam aimed and fired. The ball sailed through the rim.

"This is my cousin Marco," Sam said. He tried to talk slowly, but it was hard. "Marco, this is Billy, Chris, Rosie, Tommy, and Freddy."

Billy shot Marco the ball. Marco caught it on his head and bounced it up and down like a seal. Everyone started to laugh at him. Sam's face got hot. He grabbed the ball and made another basket.

Chris caught the ball under the net. He threw it to Marco.

This time Marco caught the ball on his knee and bounced it up and down.

Again everyone laughed at him.

Sam felt awful. “Let’s go home,” he told Marco.

The next day Sam and Marco went to school together. At recess they played kickball. When the ball came to Marco, he stopped it with his feet.

"Don't you ever use your arms?" asked Freddy. But Marco didn't understand. The next time the ball came to him, he stopped it with his feet again.

Back home Sam tried to explain the rules of sports to Marco.

"Hold the ball in your hands," said Sam. "When you play basketball, bounce the ball as you run. It's called dribbling."

But Marco just looked at Sam. He didn't understand English. He couldn't even say Sam's name right. He said Sammee.

The next day after school, Sam didn't want to go outside. He didn't want to play ball. He was afraid his friends would make fun of Marco.

"Why don't you draw?" Sam's mother asked. So Sam got out his crayons. He drew a picture of a basketball player. Marco drew a picture of his mother and father.

Sam's mother looked at the pictures. "You know what I think?" she said. "I think Marco's homesick. Let's take him to the mall to cheer him up."

At the mall Sam's mother bought Marco a Giants shirt. But it didn't make Marco happy. He didn't know who the Giants were.

"Let's try some video games," said Sam. "Watch. I'll show you how to play." Sam played Pac-Man and got a very high score. "Now you go," he said to Marco. "Don't worry if you don't get a good score at first."

Marco played Pac-Man and got a better score than Sam. He laughed. "In Mexico is Pac-Man also," he said. Marco beat Sam at every game in the arcade.

They walked farther down the mall, looking at stores. When they came to the sports store, Sam stopped to look at footballs. But Marco wasn't interested in footballs. He ran over to a display of black and white balls in boxes. Suddenly he was grinning from ear to ear.

"Why didn't I think of this before?" said Sam's mom. "Most kids in Mexico play soccer."

“Soccer? Nobody plays that around here,” said Sam.

“Well, maybe they will now,” said his mother with a smile.

Back home Marco took his new ball outside. He bounced it on his head. He kicked it around with his feet.

Chris and Billy came over. Marco kicked the ball to Chris. Chris caught it with his hands.

"No hands," said Marco.

He kicked the ball to Billy. Billy caught it with his hands too.

"No hands!" yelled Marco. "Head! Head!" He bounced the ball on his head.

Then Marco kicked the ball to Sam. Sam let the ball fall on his head.

"¡Bueno!" cried Marco. "¡Bueno, Sammee!"

Sam laughed. He kicked the ball back to Marco, who kicked it to Billy. Billy bounced it back to Sam with his head.

"¡Bueno, Billy!" said Marco. Then he kicked the ball to Chris.

Chris caught it on his head and bounced it to Billy. Billy caught it on his head and bounced it to Sam.

“This is awesome!” said Sam.

“Let’s bring the ball to school tomorrow,” said Chris.

“We’ll show the other kids how to play,” said Billy.

“¡Bueno!” said Marco. “Good!”

The next day at recess Marco showed the other second graders how to play soccer. They stood in a circle and passed the ball around with their heads. Once Sam caught the ball with his hands.

“No hands!” yelled Marco.

The next time someone caught the ball with his hands, everyone yelled, “NO HANDS!” It was fun.

Then Marco told them to pass the ball with their feet. Once Chris picked up the ball with his hands. "NO HANDS!" everyone shouted.

The third graders came by and laughed. "No hands?" they said. "What a weird game."

Some of the second graders felt stupid. They didn't like to be teased by third graders.

"Forget it," said Sam. "I've got a plan. Let's practice all week. Then we'll challenge the third graders to a game. They beat us in football. They beat us in basketball. And they beat us in baseball. But they won't beat us in soccer, will they?"

The second graders liked the plan. They practiced all week. Sam practiced most of all.

On Friday morning Sam went up to the third graders in the playground. "If you think you're so hot," he said, "play soccer with us at lunch. Then we'll see who's really hot."

The third graders took the challenge. Then everyone went back to class. It was hard to study.

Billy said 5 plus 4 was 8.

Chris dropped his notebook on the floor and all his papers fell out.

Marco was so excited he forgot the capital of the United States. He said it was Dallas, Texas.

Sam was so excited, he could hardly write his spelling words.

Finally it was lunchtime. Everyone ate quickly and rushed outside.

The second and third graders met on the field. Sam marked the goals with jackets. Billy went over the rules. "Only the goalie can catch the ball," he said. "To score you have to kick the ball past the goalie and into the place marked by jackets."

The game began. Marco passed the ball to Chris. Chris started to dribble the ball up the field. One of the third graders ran in front of him. Chris passed the ball to Sam.

Sam kicked the ball hard but missed. The ball sat on the field. A third grader ran up and kicked it way down the field.

What a kick! The third graders were really big and strong. Another third grader kicked and scored a goal. The score was 1-0. The third graders were ahead.

Sam looked worried.

"No problema," said Marco. He dribbled the ball to the opposite goal all by himself. Third graders tried to get the ball away from Marco, but he zigzagged around them. Two of the third graders fell down trying to catch Marco.

"Go, Marco baby!" yelled Billy.

Marco kicked the ball at the goal. It went in! Now the score was a 1-1 tie.

"Hooray!" shouted Sam.

The third graders had the ball now. One of them kicked it halfway down the field. Another one dribbled it to the goal. He took aim and fired. Tommy, who was goalie for the second graders, caught the ball.

"Hooray!" shouted Sam again. He knew it was all right for Tommy to catch the ball. In soccer, goalies are the only players who can do that.

Tommy threw the ball to Sam. Sam passed it to Marco. Marco ran it down to the other end and passed it back to Sam. Sam gave it a good hard kick. The ball sailed over the goalie's head. Now the score was 2-1.

The third graders weren't used to losing. They began to make mistakes. They caught the ball with their hands. Every time they did, the second graders shouted, "NO HANDS!"

The second graders started scoring like crazy. Bam! Chris got a goal. Slam! He got another one. Wham! Wham! Wham! Billy got one goal, and Rosie got two.

But Sam and Marco were the team stars. They ran circles around the third graders. They scored six goals each. When lunchtime was over, the score was 19-1.

"A wipe-out!" said Sam.

The third graders were good losers. They all shook hands with the second graders. Then they asked Marco if he would teach them how to play better.

"Sí," said Marco. "Soccer Sammee teach you too."

Everybody laughed. "Soccer Sammee!" they shouted. "Soccer Sammee!"

And that's how Sam got his nickname. At first he wasn't sure if he liked it or not.

"Is bueno?" asked Marco. "You like new name?"

Sam looked at his cousin. He knew that anything Marco gave him, he would like. "Sí," said Sam. "I like. Gracias."

Reader's Response ~ How would you feel about playing a brand new game you have never played before?

Did You Know That...?

Long ago. . .

- A game like soccer, called Zu Qiu, was probably played in China over 2,000 years ago.
- Children played soccer in the streets of London, England, more than 800 years ago.

Today. . .

- In the Dallas-Fort Worth area of Texas, thousands of girls and boys play on soccer teams.
- Soccer is called football in most countries but not in the United States. Do you know why?

What other facts do you know about soccer?

WILLIE'S
Not the Hugging Kind

by Joyce Durham Barrett
illustrated by Pat Cummings

Willie wanted someone to hug. That's what he wanted more than anything.

But no one hugged Willie. Not anymore.

Not even his daddy when he dropped Willie and his friend Jo-Jo off at school. Now, he just patted Willie on the head and said, "See you around, Son."

Willie didn't like to be patted on the head. It made him feel like a little dog. Besides, hugging felt much nicer, no matter what Jo-Jo said.

Every day Jo-Jo rode to school in the linen truck with Willie and his daddy. And when Willie used to hug his daddy good-bye, Jo-Jo would turn his head and laugh. "What did you do that for? Man, that's silly," Jo-Jo would say once they had crawled out of the truck.

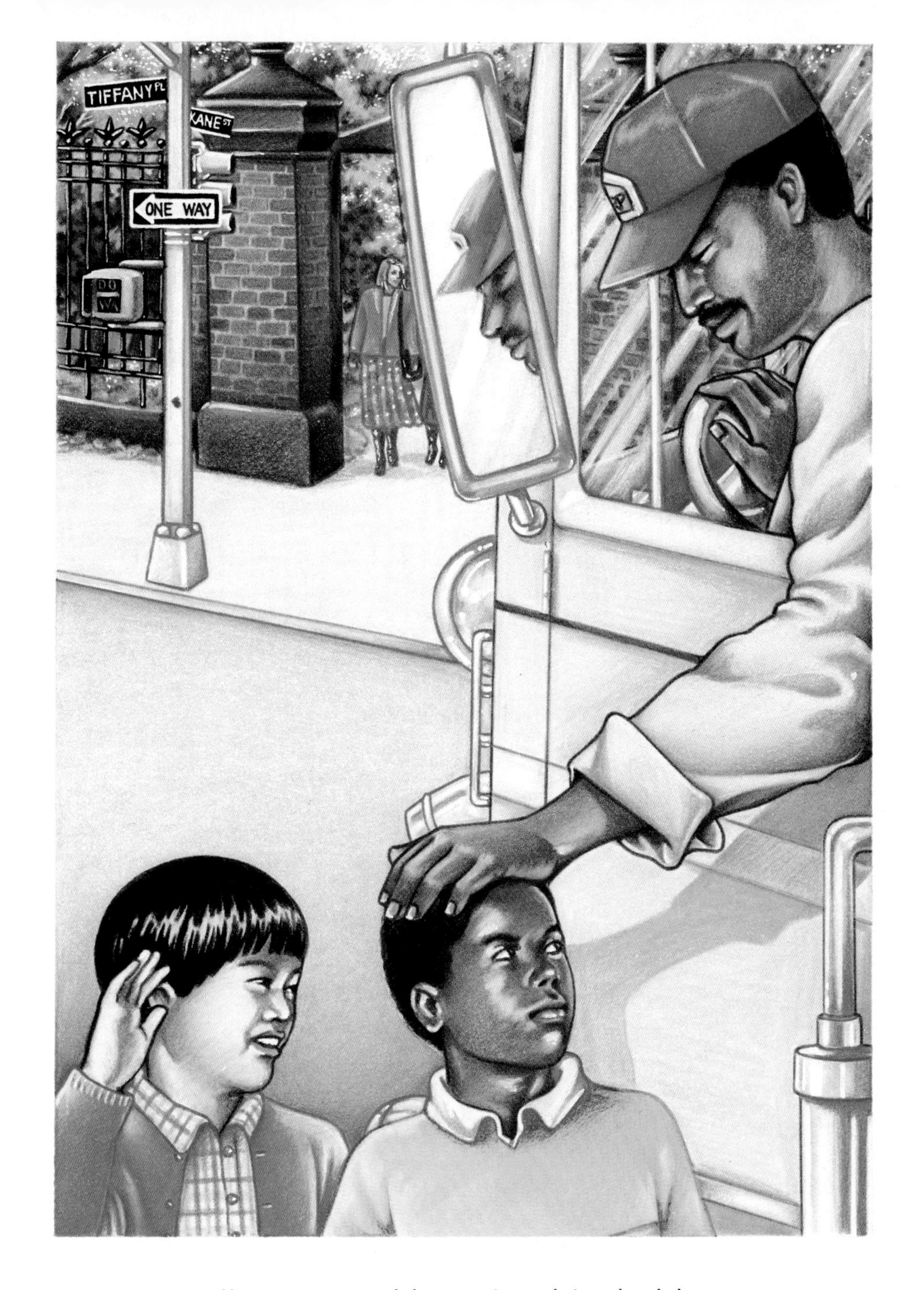

So Willie stopped hugging his daddy. He never hugged his mama or his sister anymore either. And when they tried to hug Willie, he turned away. But Willie wanted someone to hug. That's what he wanted more than anything.

12
1
2
3
4
5
6
7
8
9
10
11

At school he watched as Miss Mary put her arms around some boy or girl. It didn't look silly. Except when she tried to hug Jo-Jo. Jo-Jo made a big commotion that made everyone laugh. He wriggled and squirmed, and shrieked, "Help! Help! I'm being mugged! Help!"

At night Willie watched his sister pull her teddy bear to her and hug it. She looked so safe and happy lying there with her arms around the bear.

"Why do you hug that old thing?" Willie said. "That's silly."

Rose frowned at Willie. "Who says?" she demanded.

"Jo-Jo says, that's who says," Willie boasted.

"Well, if you ask me, I think Jo-Jo's silly," said Rose. "Besides," she said, squeezing the bear to her, "Homer's nice."

But the next night Willie pinched his nose and said, "What a smelly old bear! I wouldn't hug that old thing for a hundred dollars. Not even for a million dollars. That's silly."

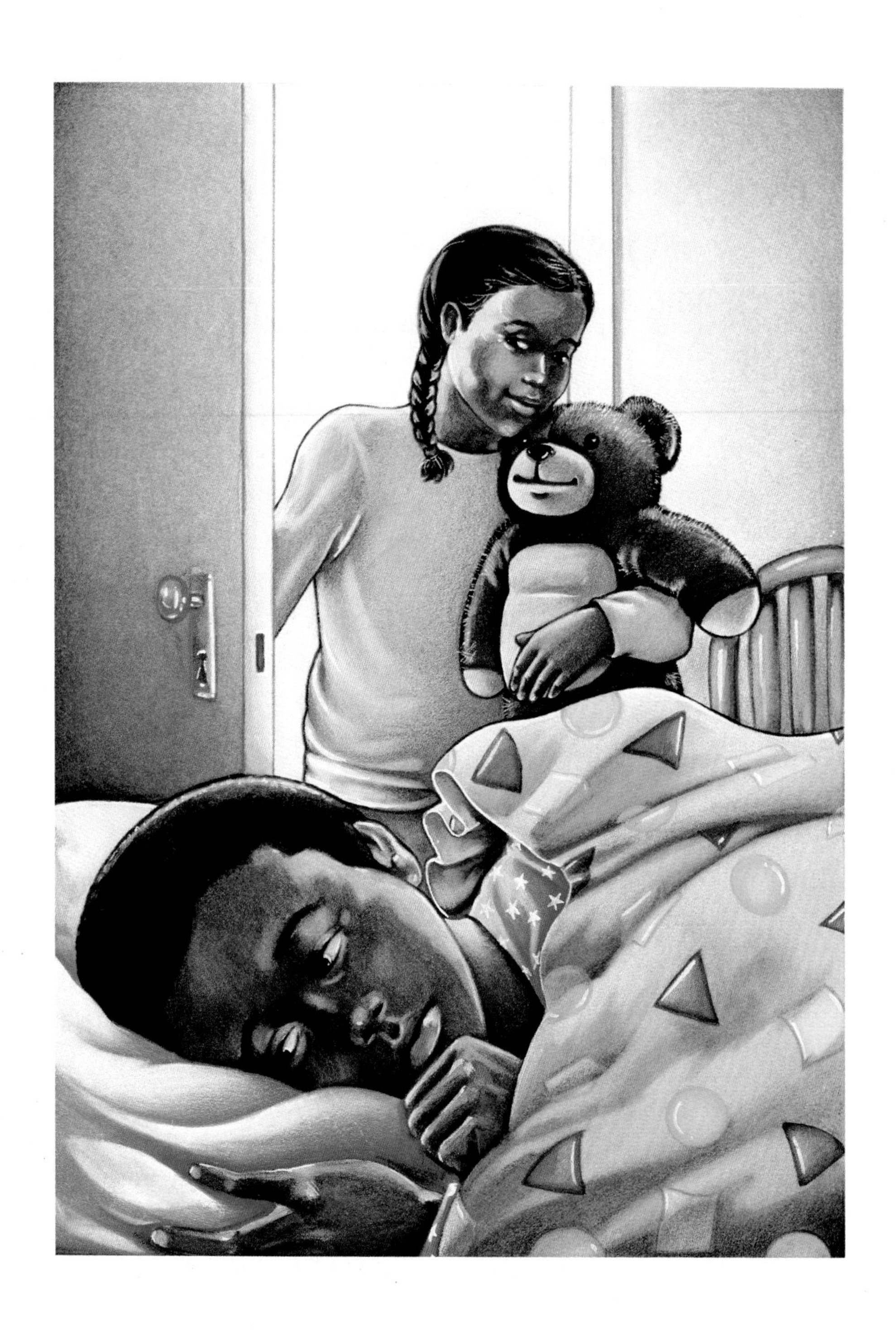

Rose pulled Homer in closer to her. "Willie," she said, "you're just not the hugging kind, then... if that's how you feel."

Willie flipped over in bed without even saying, "Good night, sleep tight, God keep you all right." And his mind went around and around on what his sister had said. The words tick-tocked back and forth with the clock sitting on the table by his bed:

NOT-the hugging kind,
NOT-the hugging kind,
NOT-the hugging kind,
if-THAT'S-how-you-feel.

But that was not how Willie felt. More than anything, Willie wanted to be the hugging kind.

Willie watched each morning as his daddy hugged first his mama and then Rose. He remembered how safe and happy he always felt with his daddy's strong arms around him.

He remembered how good it felt to put his arms around his mama. She smelled a little like lemon and a little like the lilac powder in the bathroom. She felt big and a little lumpy. She also felt soft and safe and warm.

One morning Willie went into the kitchen and everyone was hugging everyone else. But no one hugged Willie. They didn't even see him. Willie waited, hoping someone would put their arms around him. If they did, maybe he wouldn't slip away.

But no one tried. Rose just said, when she saw Willie watching, "You know that Willie says he isn't the hugging kind now. He says it's all too, too silly."

"I did not!" said Willie, bristling. "Jo-Jo said that!"

"Oh, but you said it too, Little Brother," Rose said, laughing and tousling his hair.

Willie grabbed his lunch and his books, and ran out the door to meet Jo-Jo. "Let's get out of here!" Willie shrieked, breaking into a run. "They're mugging everybody in there!"

That afternoon Jo-Jo's mother picked him up after school, so Willie walked home alone.

He walked through the park and saw a young couple standing on the footbridge with their arms around each other.

He walked down Myrtle Street and saw a woman and a man rushing down the steps from their porch to greet some visitors with hugs all around.

It seemed so long since Willie had had a hug.

He walked into the long, low branches of a willow tree and wrapped his arms around it. A blue jay flew down from a purple plum tree, and Willie reached out to its fluttering wings. He walked up to a stop sign and hugged it.

He hugged his bike in the front yard. He hugged the door to his house when he opened it. And he rushed inside to hug his mama. But she was too busy running the vacuum over the floors. Willie was kind of glad. After all, he felt a little silly.

That night, after Willie had had his bath, he took the old bath towel and draped it across the head of his bed.

"What's that for?" Rose asked, hugging Homer to her.

"Nothing," said Willie.

The next night Willie put the old bath towel on the bed again. And the next night, and the next. Each night, when he was sure that Rose was not watching, he slipped the old towel down from the headboard and he hugged it. But it didn't feel soft and safe and warm.

Willie wanted to hug someONE, not someTHING.

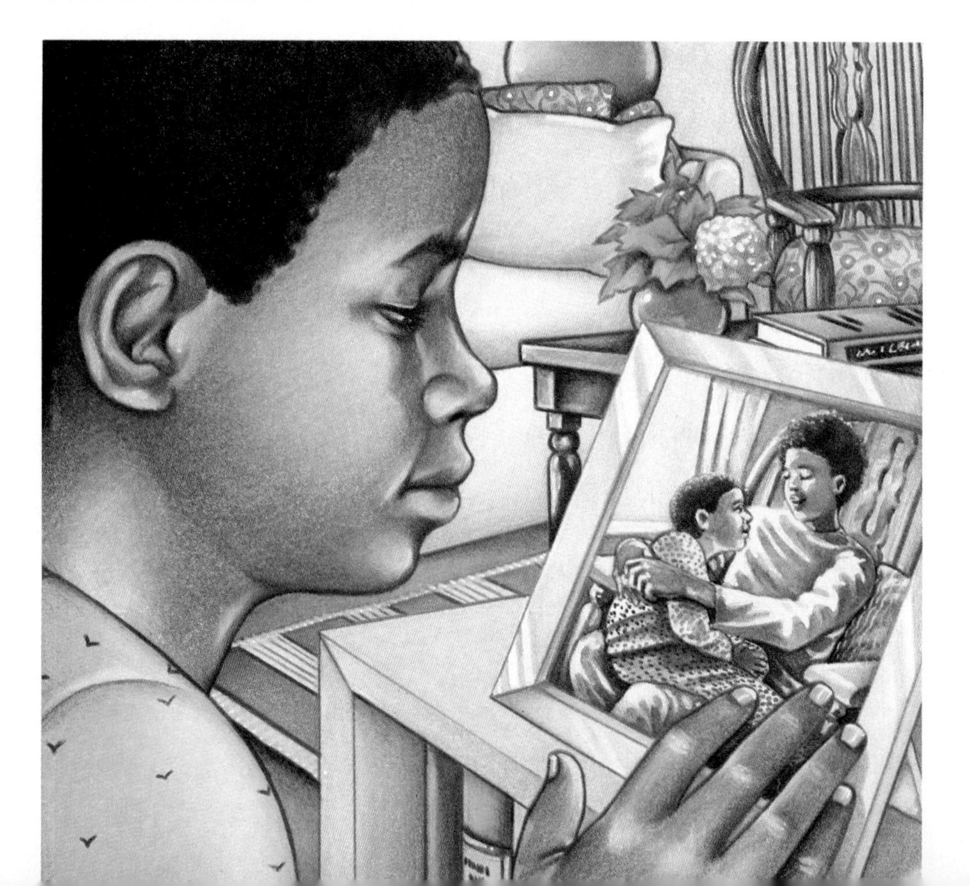

In the morning Willie's mama was in the kitchen making biscuits. He watched Rose brush up to her and put her arms around her.

When the biscuits were finished and browning in the oven, Willie went up and put his arms around his mama too. Or almost around her. There was a little more to her than he remembered. She felt much nicer than an old towel. And, even better, she hugged back.

"What's all this, Willie," she said, "hugging around here on me so early in the morning?"

"Yeah, Willie," said Rose. "I thought all that hugging was too, too silly."

Willie clung tighter to his mama.

"That's all right," said his mama. "Willie knows, don't you, Son, that it's them that don't get hugging who think it's silly."

Willie looked up into his mama's face, smiling, until he felt a tap on his shoulder. Turning, he saw his daddy smiling down at him. "My turn, Son," he said.

Willie put his arms around his daddy, burying his face in the familiar khaki shirt and feeling once again secure in the warmth of the strong arms around him.

Breakfast tasted better to Willie than it had in many a day. And when it came time to leave for school, Willie gave hugs all around.

Jumping into the big truck, Willie and his daddy stopped by to pick up Jo-Jo. When they arrived at school, Willie reached up and gave his daddy a quick, tight hug. Then he scooted out the door behind Jo-Jo.

"What did you do that for, man?" Jo-Jo said, once they were out of the truck. "Don't you know that's silly?"

Willie gave his friend a shove on the shoulder. Maybe Jo-Jo wouldn't let someone hug him, but he would allow a playful shove now and then. "Go on, now, Jo-Jo," he said. "I think *you're* what's silly."

Jo-Jo ran on ahead. "Help, help!" he shrieked. "I'm being mugged! Help!"

But Willie didn't mind. He lagged behind, feeling warm and safe knowing that he was, after all, the hugging kind.

Reader's Response ~ Are you the hugging kind? If so, whom do you like to hug?

YOU CAN SIGN IT

Willie finds out that hugging is a great way of saying that he loves his family. We all have different ways of telling each other what we think and what we feel. We use words or sometimes, like Willie, we use actions.

People who can't hear have a special language called Ameslan, which is short for American Sign Language. The movements of their hands stand for ideas, words, or letters.

Look at the girl signing a message. Do you think it's what Willie was trying to say?

DANDELION

STORY AND PICTURES BY

Don Freeman

On a sunny Saturday morning Dandelion woke up, stretched and yawned, and jumped out of bed.

After doing his daily exercises Dandelion looked out of the window, blinked his eyes, and said, "I wonder if the mail has come?"

He put on his sweater and went outside to the mailbox. There was a letter, and it was written in fancy gold ink!

Dandelion was very excited. "Why, that's today!" he said. "It's a good thing I planned to get a haircut!"

As soon as he had washed and dried the breakfast dishes and made his bed nice and neat, he ran down the street to the barbershop.

Lou Kangaroo had a chair waiting for him. First he trimmed Dandelion's hair, and then gave him a shampoo.

Dandelion thought he should have a manicure too.

When Lou Kangaroo had finished Dandelion looked a bit foolish.

His mane was frizzy and fuzzy and completely unrulish.

"Maybe a wave would help," Lou suggested, showing him a picture in the latest fashion magazine for lions.

Dandelion agreed. This was exactly what he needed.

So Lou went about curling his mane.

He looked magnificent!

But now Dandelion thought he really should wear something more elegant than a sweater to the party.

"This jacket is the very newest style," said Theodore the Tailor, "and it just fits you. All you need now is a cap and a cane. Happy Crane will be glad to help you."

What a dapper dandy he had suddenly become!

"It's nearly half-past three!" said Dandelion. "I've just time to get something for my hostess!"

A bouquet of dandelions would be perfect.

He knew this tall door very well, having been here many times before.

He rang the bell.

When Jennifer Giraffe opened the door she looked very surprised. "Yes?" she said. "What can I do for you?"

"Why, I've come to your party," he answered.

“Oh, I’m sorry, sir, but you are not anyone I know!” said Miss Giraffe. “You must have come to the wrong address.”

And with this she closed the door right in poor Dandelion's face!

"I'm Dandelion!" he roared. "You've made a mighty mistake!" But there was no use knocking. The door stayed tight shut.

Dandelion began walking back and forth. Back and forth, up and down the long block he paced.

And as he paced, the sky grew dark. Then a sudden gust of wind sprang up and blew away his beautiful bouquet, and his snappy cap flew off!

To make matters worse, it began to rain in torrents. Dandelion dropped his cane and stood under a weeping willow tree.

But the rain poured down through the branches. Dandelion was soon soaking wet and his curls came unfurled.

He took off his jacket and hung it on a willow branch. Luckily he had kept on his sweater.

At last the rain stopped
and the warm sunshine
came beaming down.

Dandelion decided to sit on Jennifer
Giraffe's front steps until his mane was dry.

While he sat there waiting
he spied three dandelion flowers
under the bottom step where
they had been protected from
the wind and the rain.

He picked the dandelions and said,
"I think I will try again."

And he rang the bell.

"Well, well! If it isn't our friend Dandelion at last!" said Jennifer Giraffe. "We've been waiting for you for the past hour. I do hope you weren't caught in that awful cloudburst!"

Everyone at the party greeted him heartily.

Later on when all her guests were enjoying tea and taffy, Jennifer Giraffe told Dandelion about the silly-looking lion who had come to the door earlier.

Dandelion almost spilled his cup of tea as he reared back and laughed uproariously, "Oh, that was me! I was that silly-looking lion!"

Miss Giraffe was so flustered she got herself all tangled up in her long pearl necklace. "I do apologize for having closed the door on you!" she said, blushing. "I promise never to do such a thing again!"

"And I promise you I will never again try to turn myself into a stylish dandy," said Dandelion as he sipped his tea. "From now on I'll always be just plain me!"

Reader's Response ~ When you go to a party, how do you decide what to wear?

◆ Near and Far ◆

People say,
"It could only happen here."

Why does it matter where
a story takes place?

Unit 2 Theme

MEMORIAL WINDOW, *by Louis Tiffany, Tiffany Studios, stained glass, American c. 1905.*
© The Metropolitan Museum of Art, New York, Anonymous Gift in memory of Mr. and Mrs. A. B. Frank, 1981 (1981.159)

Theme Books for Near and Far

***E**xciting places can be as near as a new store or as far away as the moon. You don't have to wait to visit an exciting place. All you have to do is open a book!*

✽ What do you think happens when a mailman trades places with a spaceman? You'll laugh when you read ***Mr. Munday and the Space Creatures*** by Bonnie Pryor.

✽ Have you ever thought about flying high in the sky? Then you will like traveling with Rosalba and her *abuela*, her grandmother, in ***Abuela*** by Arthur Dorros. Watch a simple trip to the park turn into a flying adventure above the rooftops of New York City.

More Books to Enjoy

When I Was Young in the Mountains by Cynthia Rylant

Three Days on a River in a Red Canoe by Vera B. Williams

The Desert Is Theirs by Byrd Baylor

Ben's Dream by Chris Van Allsburg

TRAIN SONG

by Diane Siebert
paintings by Mike Wimmer

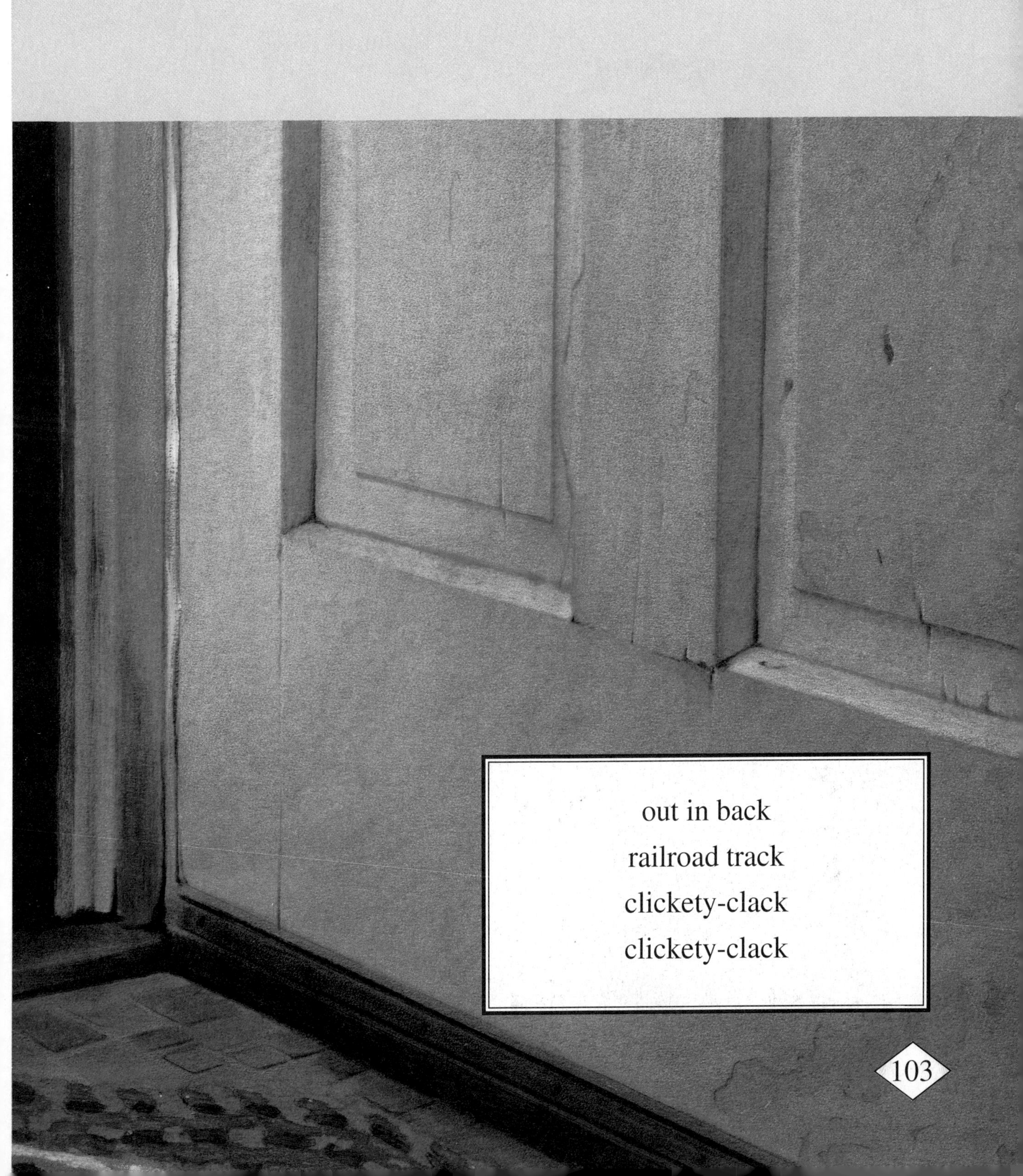

out in back
railroad track
clickety-clack
clickety-clack

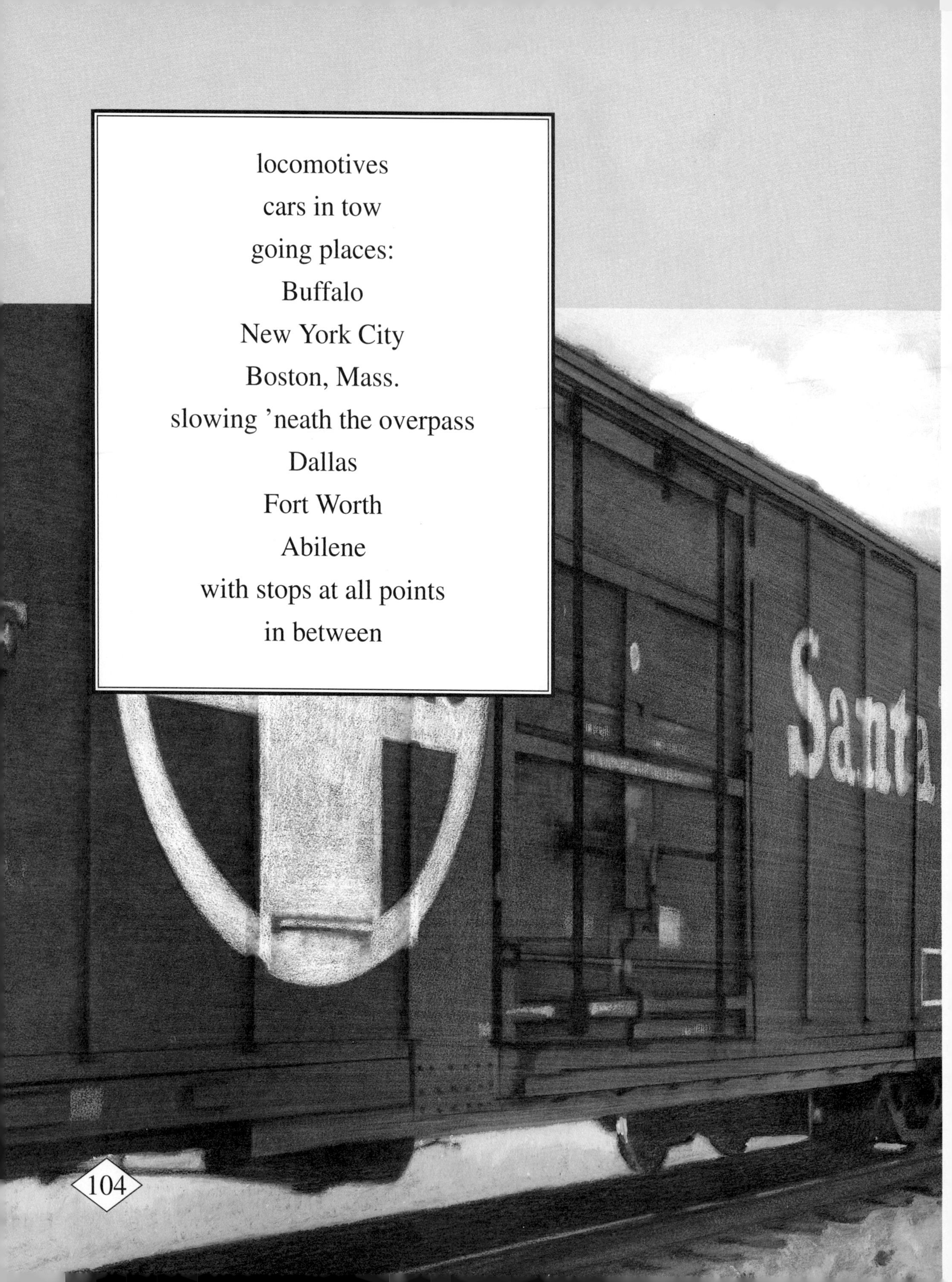

locomotives
cars in tow
going places:
Buffalo
New York City
Boston, Mass.
slowing 'neath the overpass
Dallas
Fort Worth
Abilene
with stops at all points
in between

steel wheels rolling
on steel trails
rumbling
grumbling
on steel rails

engineers with striped hats
head-of-the-line aristocrats
up in front
sitting high
see them wave as they go by

great trains
freight trains
talk about your late trains
the 509
right on time
straight through to L.A.
whistle blows
there she goes
slicing through the day

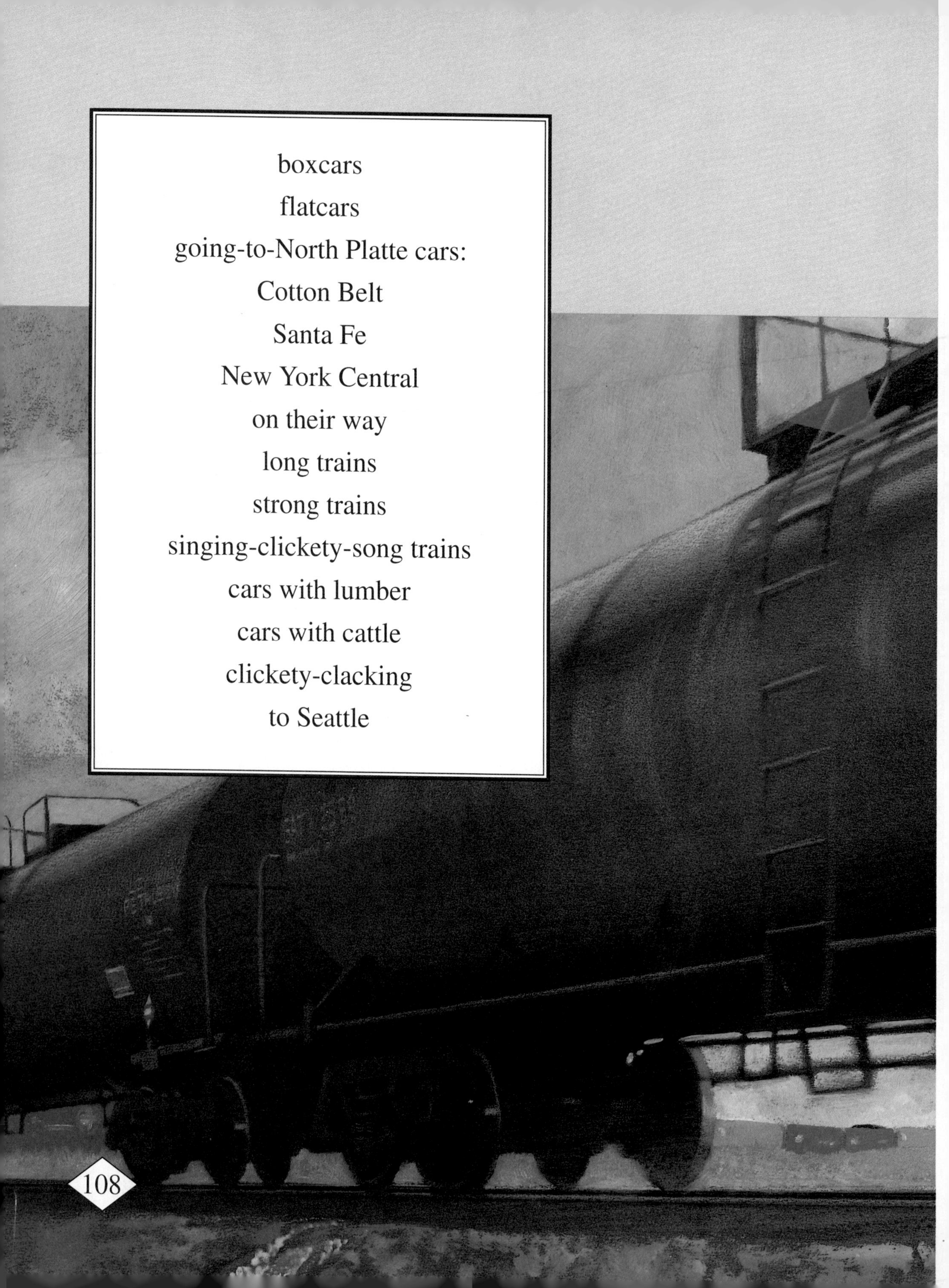

boxcars
flatcars
going-to-North Platte cars:
Cotton Belt
Santa Fe
New York Central
on their way
long trains
strong trains
singing-clickety-song trains
cars with lumber
cars with cattle
clickety-clacking
to Seattle

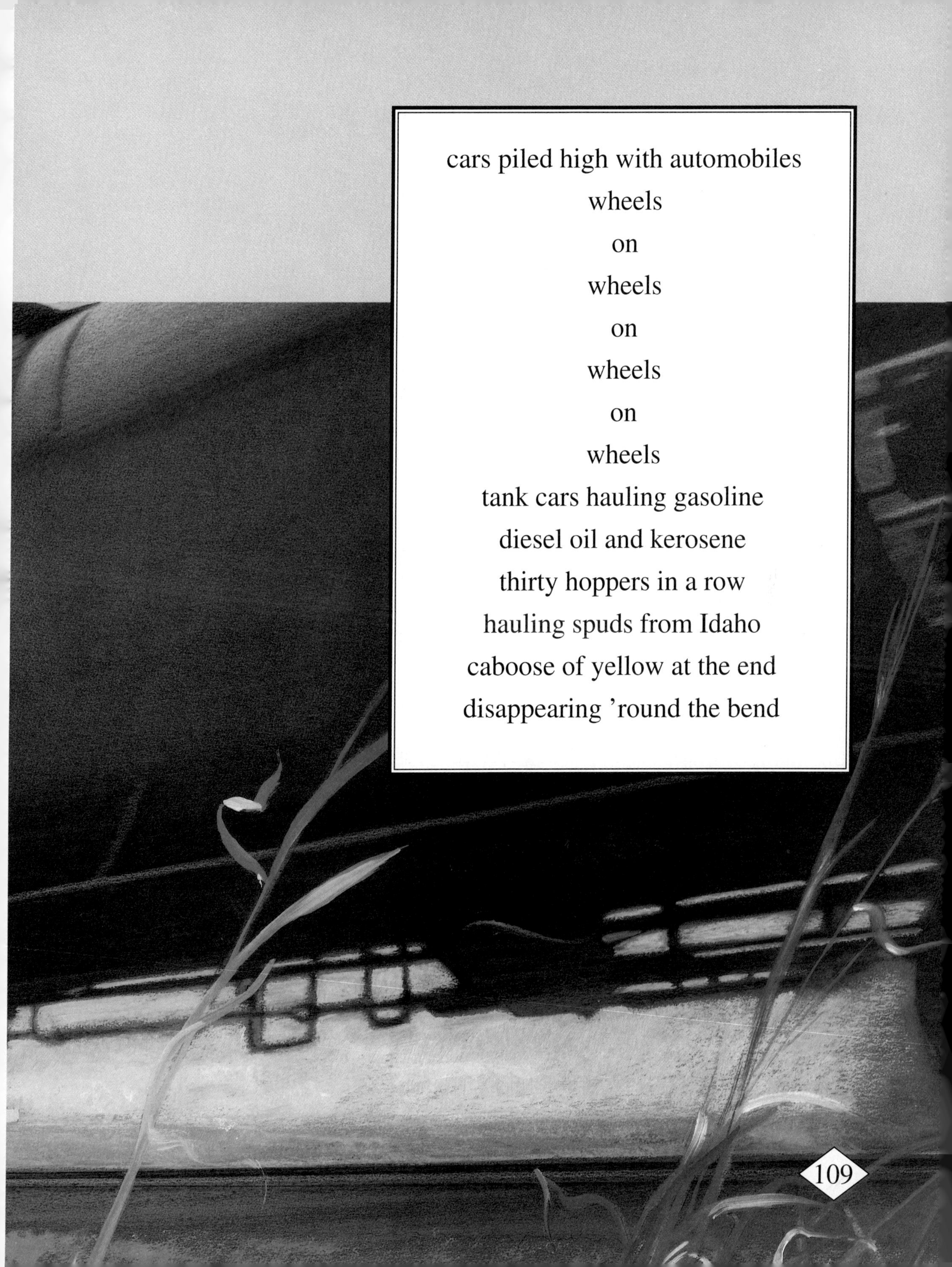

cars piled high with automobiles
wheels
on
wheels
on
wheels
on
wheels
tank cars hauling gasoline
diesel oil and kerosene
thirty hoppers in a row
hauling spuds from Idaho
caboose of yellow at the end
disappearing ’round the bend

trains with passengers on board
clickety-clacking
rolling toward
their destinations far away
clickety-clacking
night and day

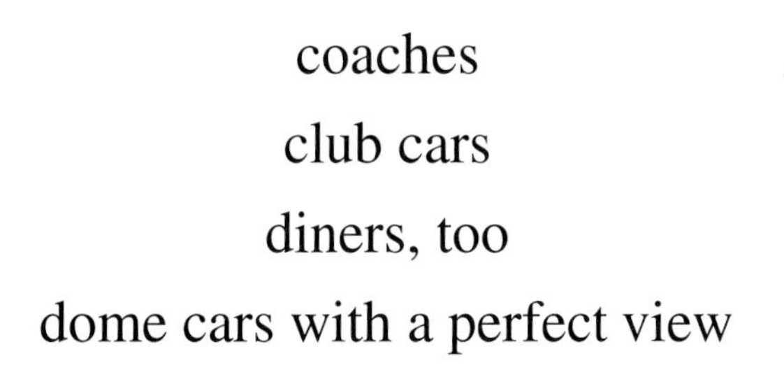
coaches
club cars
diners, too
dome cars with a perfect view

signal lights
green
yellow
red
railroad station up ahead

rolling
rolling
into town
toward the platform
slowing down
creaking
clanking
air brakes squeal
moaning
groaning
steel on steel

TICKETS

Overnighter to the bay
arrive at noon on Saturday
get a sleeper
don't be late
she's waiting on Track number 8

head conductor
dressed in black
peering up and down the track
checks his watch
now hear him shout:
"ALL ABOARD"
she's pulling out!

through the tunnel
going fast
clickety-clack
she's roaring past
the cities, suburbs, little towns
past forest greens and desert browns

spikes and crossties
smooth, worn rails
through the twilight
whistle wails
feel the rhythm
hear the sound
clickety-clacking
homeward bound

say good night

and

wave good-bye

hear the railroad lullaby

Reader's Response ~ What would you like most about traveling on a train?

Rolling Cars

If you ever see a freight train rolling over the tracks, you might wonder what's in all those cars.

A boxcar is covered on every side. It carries things like toys, TVs, and furniture. Refrigerated boxcars can carry food.

A tank car carries liquids. It might carry gasoline, molasses, vegetable oil, or paint. Tank cars are loaded at the top and unloaded from the bottom.

Hopper cars carry grain, rock, chemicals, sand, and fertilizer. Covered hoppers have hatches on top for filling and on the bottom for emptying.

How My Parents Learned to Eat

written by
Ina R. Friedman

illustrated by
Allen Say

In our house, some days we eat with chopsticks and some days we eat with knives and forks.

For me, it's natural.

When my mother met my father, she was a Japanese schoolgirl and he was an American sailor. His ship was stationed in Yokohama.

American Library Association 1984

Every day, my father, whose name is John, walked in the park with my mother, Aiko. They sat on a bench and talked. But my father was afraid to invite my mother to dinner.

If we go to a restaurant, he thought, I'll go hungry because I don't know how to eat with chopsticks. And if I go hungry, I'll act like a bear. Then Aiko won't like me. I'd better not ask her to dinner.

My mother wondered why my father never invited her to dinner. Perhaps John is afraid I don't know how to eat with a knife and fork and I'll look silly, she thought. Maybe it is best if he doesn't invite me to dinner.

So they walked and talked and never ate a bowl of rice or a piece of bread together.

One day, the captain of my father's ship said, "John, in three weeks the ship is leaving Japan."

My father was sad. He wanted to marry my mother. How can I ask her to marry me? he thought. I don't even know if we like the same food. And if we don't, we'll go hungry. It's hard to be happy if you're hungry. I'll have to find out what food she likes. And I'll have to learn to eat with chopsticks.

So he went to a Japanese restaurant.

Everyone sat on cushions around low tables. My father bowed to the waiter. "Please, teach me to eat with chopsticks."

"Of course," said the waiter, bowing.

The waiter brought a bowl of rice and a plate of sukiyaki. Sukiyaki is made of small pieces of meat, vegetables, and tofu. It smelled good. My father wanted to gobble it up.

The waiter placed two chopsticks between my father's fingers. "Hold the bottom chopstick still. Move the top one to pick up the food," the waiter said.

My father tried, but the meat slipped off his chopstick and fell on his lap.

The waiter came back with a bowl of soup. How can I eat soup with chopsticks? my father thought.

"Drink," said the waiter. "Drink from the bowl."

"Thank goodness," my father said. After the soup my father felt better. He picked up the chopsticks. Finally, my father put one piece of meat in his mouth. Delicious!

"More soup, please," he said.

After three bowls of soup my father felt much better. Then he practiced some more with his chopsticks. Soon, there was more sukiyaki in his belly than on the floor. But it was too late to call my mother. He had to run back to his ship.

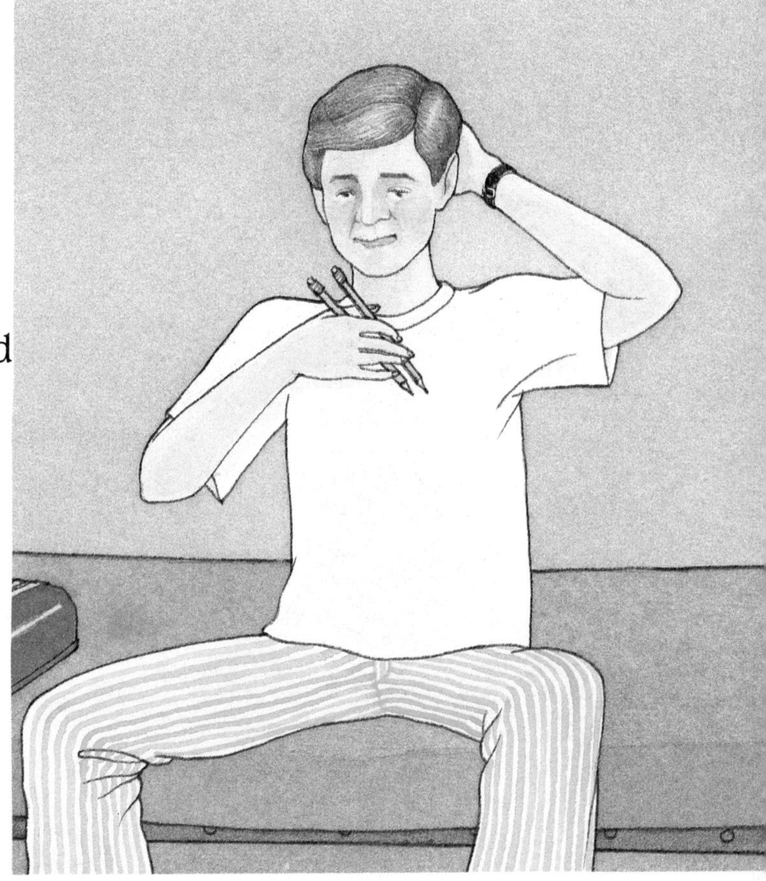

That night, my mother was sad. Every other day my father had come to see her. That day he did not come. He did not call on the telephone. Perhaps he was tired of walking and talking. Perhaps he was ashamed of her because she did not know how to eat with a knife and fork. Perhaps his ship had sailed away. All night she could not sleep.

And all night my father sat on his bunk, pretending to pick up sukiyaki.

The next morning my father called my mother. "Please, will you eat dinner with me tonight?"

"Yes!" my mother shouted into the phone. First she was happy. Then she was afraid. She took her schoolbooks and ran to the house of Great Uncle.

Great Uncle had visited England. He had seen the British Museum. He had eaten dinners with Englishmen.

My mother knocked at the door. Great Uncle opened it.

"Why are you so sad, child?" he asked.

"Because I must learn to eat with a knife and fork by seven o'clock tonight."

Great Uncle nodded. "Foreign ways are quite strange. Why do you want to eat with a knife and fork?"

My mother blushed.

"Is it the American sailor?" Great Uncle asked. "I see... Here, take this note to your teacher. At lunchtime I will come and take you to a foreign restaurant. By seven o'clock tonight you will eat with a knife and fork."

My mother picked up her school bag and bowed.

"No," Great Uncle stuck out his hand. "In the West you shake hands."

The restaurant had red carpets and many lights. Great Uncle pulled out a chair for my mother. "In the West, men help ladies into chairs," he told her.

My mother looked at the small fork and the large fork on the left. She looked at the knife, little spoon, and big spoon on the right. Her head grew dizzy.

"Different utensils for different foods," Great Uncle said.

"How strange to dirty so many things," said my mother. "A chopstick is a chopstick. I can eat everything with two chopsticks."

When the waiter brought the soup, Great Uncle pointed at the large spoon. "Dip it slowly, bring it to your mouth. Sip quietly."

My mother's hand trembled. The soup spilled onto the white cloth.

"You'll learn," Great Uncle encouraged her.

When my mother was finished with the soup, the waiter brought her a plate of mashed potatoes, roast beef, and peas.

"This is the way Westerners eat," Great Uncle said. "With the knife and fork they cut the meat. Then they hold the fork upside down in their left hand. Like birds, they build a nest of mashed potatoes. They put the peas in the nest with the knife. Then they slip the nest into their mouth. Try it."

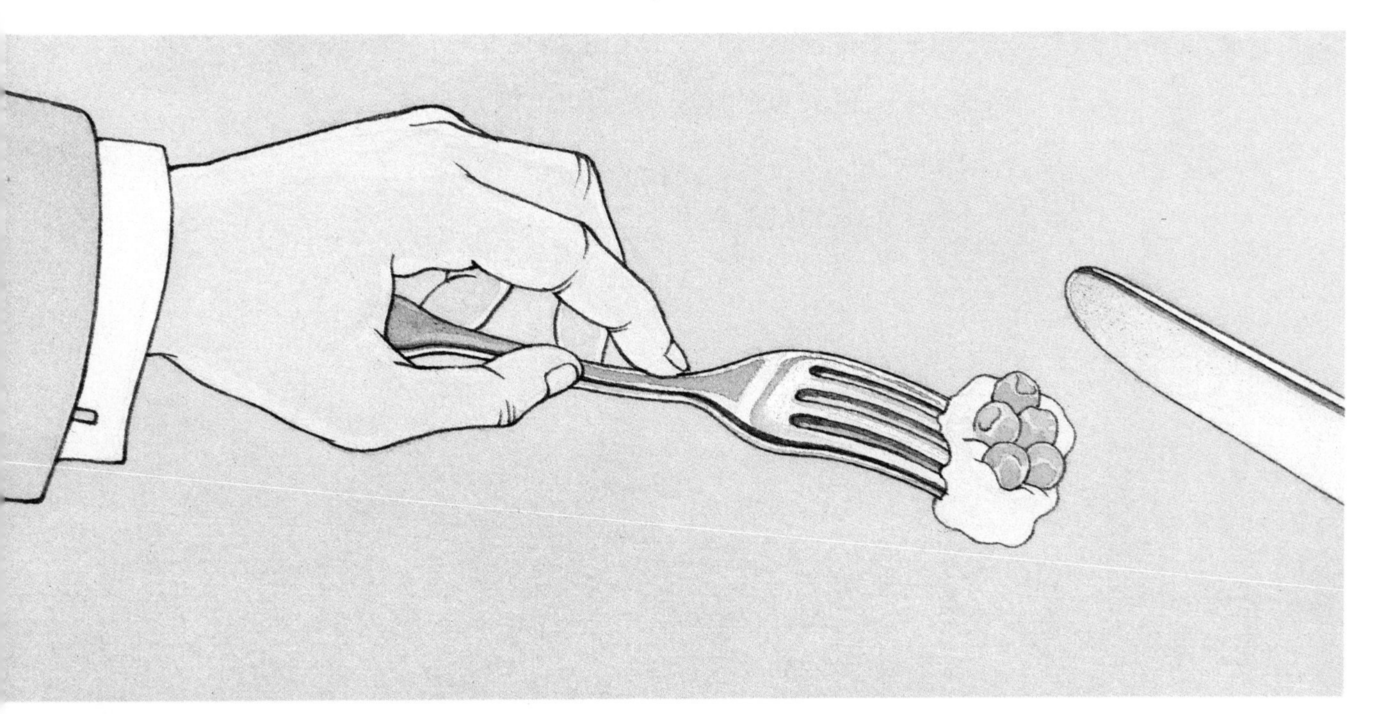

The mashed potatoes were not difficult. But the peas rolled all over the plate. "Impossible," said my mother. "I'll never learn by seven o'clock tonight."

"You can learn anything," Great Uncle said. "Try again. More mashed potatoes and peas, please," he said to the waiter.

At seven o'clock my father came to see my mother.

"Why didn't you wear your kimono?" he asked. "We are going to a Japanese restaurant."

"A Japanese restaurant? Don't you think I know how to eat Western food?" my mother asked.

"Of course. Don't you think I know how to eat Japanese food?"

"Of course."

"Then, tonight we'll eat meat and potatoes. Tomorrow night we'll eat sukiyaki."

"Tomorrow night I will wear my kimono," my mother said. She started to bow. Then she stopped and put out her hand. My father shook it.

My father ordered two plates of mashed potatoes, roast beef, and peas. He watched my mother cut the meat into pieces. He stared when she turned over her fork and made a bird's nest. He was amazed.

"You are very clever with a knife and fork," he said.

"Thank you," said my mother.

"You must teach me," my father said. "That's a new way of eating peas."

"Teach you?"

"Yes, Americans don't eat that way." He slid his fork under some peas and put them in his mouth.

My mother stared at him. "But Great Uncle taught me. He lived in England. He knows the ways of the West."

My father began to laugh. "He taught you to eat like an Englishman. Americans eat differently."

"Oh, dear," my mother said. "A chopstick is a chopstick. Everyone uses them in the same way."

"Yes. When we are married we'll eat only with chopsticks." He took her hand.

"Married! If I marry you I want to eat like an American."

"I'll teach you to eat with a knife and fork and you teach me to use chopsticks."

My mother shook my father's hand. My father bowed.

That's why at our house some days we eat with chopsticks and some days we eat with knives and forks.

Reader's Response ~ Do you think it's fun or scary to learn new ways of doing things? Explain.

Go Fish!

Allen Say, the illustrator of this story, likes to go flyfishing. What does he do, catch flies or use flies to catch fish? Neither one. Instead, he fools the fish by making them think there is a fly on his fishing hook. He ties feathers, fur, and thread around a hook to make a "fly" and floats it on the water or lets it sink. A hungry fish thinks it's getting a meal and gets hooked instead.

In *A River Dream*, a book he both wrote and illustrated, Mr. Say tells of a boy who learns to flyfish from his uncle. He finds out that there's more to flyfishing than catching a fish. What do you think he learns?

A KITE

I often sit and wish that I
Could be a kite up in the sky,
And ride upon the breeze and go
Whichever way I chanced to blow.
Then I could look beyond the town,
And see the river winding down,
And follow all the ships that sail
Like me before the merry gale,
Until at last with them I came
To some place with a foreign name.

Frank Dempster Sherman

Lee Bennett Hopkins
INTERVIEWS

Bonnie Pryor

Bonnie Pryor is a busy woman. She is the mother of six children—four girls and two boys. She owns a children's bookstore in Ohio, where she lives. And she writes many books for boys and girls.

How does such a busy person find time to write?

"I am lucky that I do not need too much sleep," she said. "I do most of my writing after midnight, when everyone else is fast asleep.

"I love to write and I love to read. You must read a lot before you can write well. Read all kinds of books. Read books about everything. Reading books by many different authors will help you make your own stories better."

The next story you are going to read, *The House on Maple Street*, is by Mrs. Pryor and is one of her favorites. This is what she would like you to know about it.

"The idea for this story came to me one day when my daughter Chrissy found an arrowhead near our house.

"I began thinking about the arrowhead. I wondered how long it had been buried in the ground before Chrissy found it.

"What would happen a thousand years from now if someone found one of your toys buried in the ground? This is something you can wonder about and write about.

"I hope this story will also start you to think about the place where you live. Has anyone lived there before? Have you seen changes since you've lived there?"

I asked Mrs. Pryor if the arrowhead her daughter found is still around.

"Yes," she said. "It is kept in a bureau drawer in my daughter's room. It will always remind us of *The House on Maple Street*."

Mrs. Pryor's stories have won awards and honors. National groups of both science and social studies teachers chose *The House on Maple Street* for their Outstanding Book Lists.

As you read *The House on Maple Street*, you might find yourself asking the kinds of questions that scientists ask about places and the people who lived there long ago.

Reader's Response ⁓ What question would you ask Bonnie Pryor if you were interviewing her?

Library Link ⁓ *You might also enjoy Bonnie Pryor's* The Porcupine Mouse*, an award-winning, humorous story about two mice who move to a new place.*

Kids Found It!

Bonnie Pryor got the idea for "The House on Maple Street" from an arrowhead her daughter found. Here are some interesting finds that other young people have made.

Harlan Price and Eli Ceryak were canoeing on the Suwannee River in Georgia when they spotted some old bones. They worked with scientists to uncover the fossil bones of a type of sea cow that is now extinct.

Students in Alabama helped scientists dig up the old town of Cahawba. They found buttons, nails, and broken pots. Their discoveries helped scientists learn about different peoples who have lived at the site during the past 400 years.

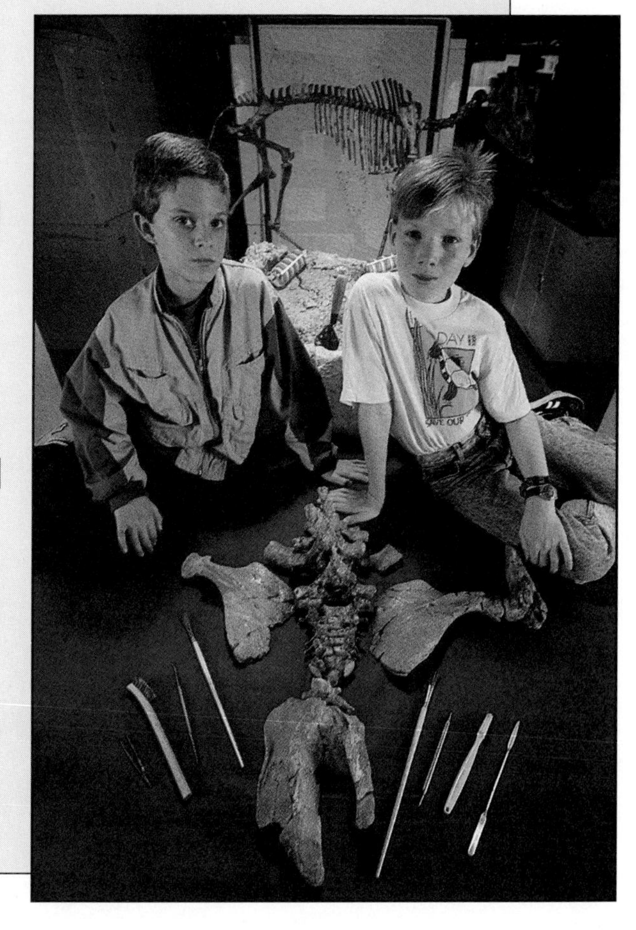

THE HOUSE ON MAPLE STREET

written *by* BONNIE PRYOR
illustrated *by* BETH PECK

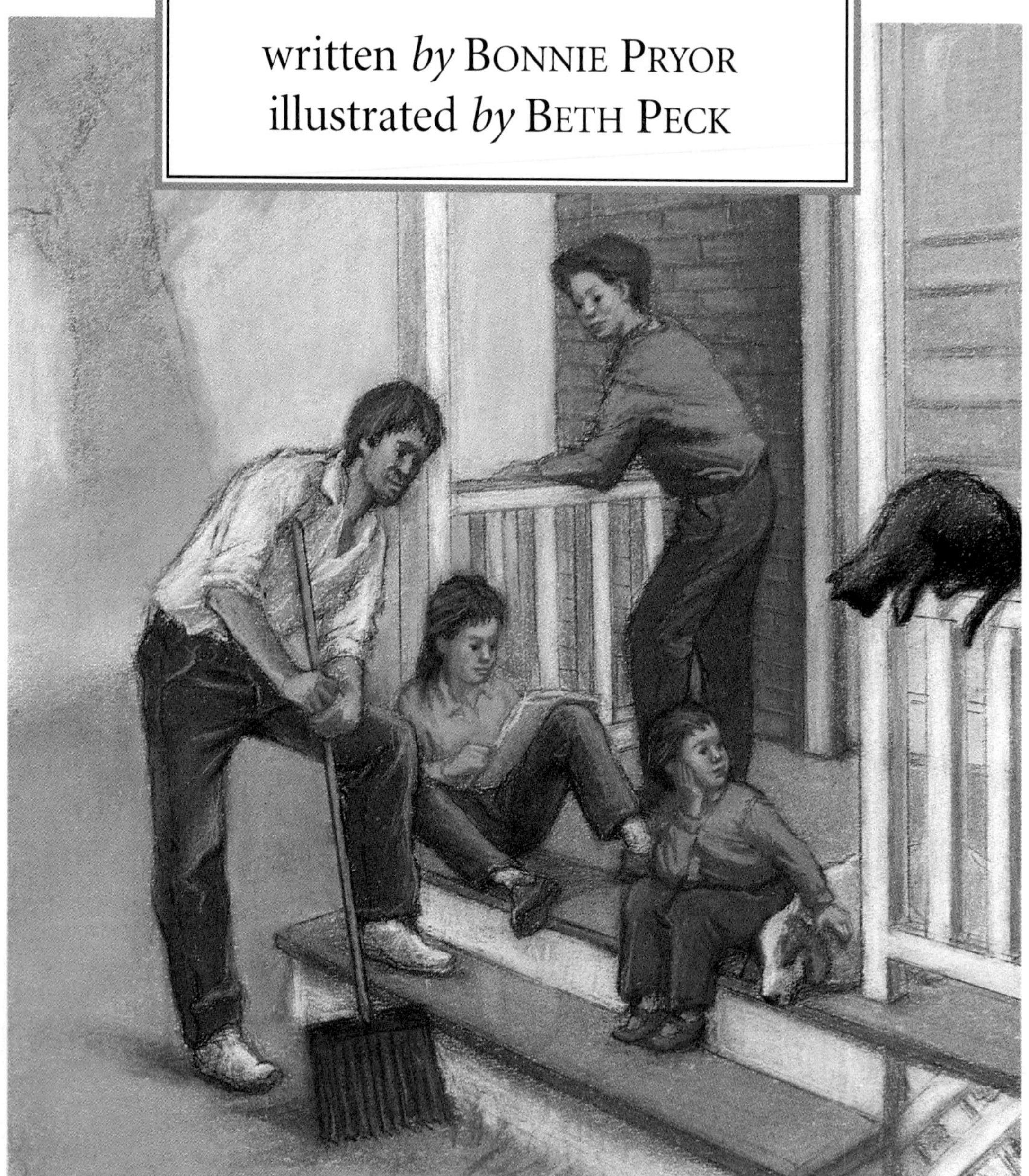

This is 107 Maple Street. Chrissy and Jenny live here with their mother and father, a dog named Maggie, and a fat cat named Sally.

Three hundred years ago there was no house here or even a street. There was only a forest and a bubbling spring where the animals came to drink.

One day a fierce storm roared across the forest. The sky rolled with thunder, and lightning crashed into a tree. A deer sniffed the air in alarm. Soon the woods were ablaze.

The next spring a few sturdy flowers poked through the ashes, and by the year after that the land was covered with grass. Some wildflowers grew at the edge of the stream where the deer had returned to drink.

One day the earth trembled, and a cloud of dust rose to the sky. A mighty herd of buffalo had come to eat the sweet grass and drink from the stream.

People came, following the buffalo herd. They set up their tepees near the stream, and because they liked it so much, they stayed for the whole summer.

One boy longed to be a great hunter like his father, but for now he could only pretend with his friends. In their games, one boy was chosen to be the buffalo.

His father taught the boy how to make an arrowhead and smooth it just so, the way his father had taught him. But the boy was young, and the day was hot.

He ran off to play with his friends and left the arrowhead on a rock. When he came back later to get it, he could not find it.

The buffalo moved on, searching for new grass, and the people packed up their tepees and followed.

For a long time the land was quiet. Some rabbits made their home in the stump of a burned tree, and a fox made a den in some rocks.

One day there was a new sound. The fox looked up. A wagon train passed by, heading for California. The settlers stopped beside the stream for a night. But they dreamed of gold and places far away and were gone the next morning.

Other wagons came, following the tracks of the first. The fox family moved into the woods, but the rabbits stayed snug in their burrows until the people had gone.

Soon after, a man and a woman camped along the stream. They were heading west, but the woman would soon have a child. They looked around them and knew it was a good place to stay. The man cut down trees and made a house.

He pulled up the tree stumps left from the fire and planted his crops. The child was a girl, and they named her Ruby and called her their little jewel.

Ruby had a set of china dishes that she played with every day. One day when she was making a mudpie on the banks of the stream, she found an arrowhead buried deep in the ground. She put it in a cup to show her father when he came in from the fields.

Ruby's mother called her to watch the new baby. While she was gone, a rabbit sniffed at the cup and knocked it off the rock. It fell into the tunnel to his burrow, and the rabbit moved away to a new home under the roots of a tree.

Ruby grew up and moved away, but her brother stayed on the farm. By now there were other people nearby, and he married a girl from another farm. They had six children, and he built a larger house so they would all fit.

Now the old wagon trail was used as a road, and the dust got into the house. When his wife complained, Ruby's brother planted a row of maple trees along the road to keep out the dust and shade the house. After the children were grown, he and his wife moved away, but one of their daughters stayed on the farm with her husband and children.

One day the children's great-aunt Ruby came for a visit. She was an old lady with snow-white hair. The children loved to hear her stories of long ago. She told them about the cup and arrowhead she had lost when she was a girl.

After she left, the children looked and looked. But they never found them, though they searched for days.

The town had grown nearly to the edge of the farm, and another man up the road filled in the stream and changed its course. For a while there was a trickle of water in the spring when the snow melted, but weeds and dirt filled in the bed, until hardly anyone remembered a stream had ever been there.

New people lived on the farm. It was the schoolteacher and his family, and they sold much of the land to others. The road was paved with bricks, so there was no longer any dust, but the maple trees remained. The branches hung down over the road, making it shady and cool. People called it Maple Street. Automobiles drove on the road, along with carts and wagons, and there were many new houses.

The house was crumbling and old, and one day some men tore it down. For a while again, the land was bare. The rabbits lived comfortably, with only an occasional owl or fox to chase them. But one day a young couple came walking along and stopped to admire the trees.

"What a wonderful place for a home," said the young woman. So they hired carpenters and masons to build a cozy house of red bricks with white trim.

The young couple lived happily in the house for several years. The young man got a job in another town, and they had to move.

The house was sold to a man and a woman who had two girls named Chrissy and Jenny and a dog named Maggie, and a fat cat named Sally.

The girls helped their father dig up a spot of ground for a garden, but it was Maggie the dog who dug up something white in the soft spring earth.

"Stop," cried Chrissy, and she picked up the tiny cup made of china. Inside was the arrowhead found and lost so long ago.

"Who lost these?" the girls wondered. Chrissy and Jenny put the cup and arrowhead on a shelf for others to see. Someday perhaps their children will play with the tiny treasures and wonder about them, too. But the cup and arrowhead will forever keep their secrets, and the children can only dream.

Reader's Response ~ What story might Chrissy and Jenny make up about the cup with an arrowhead inside it?

BROWSING FOR BOOKS

Good Books for Good Friends

When you go to a birthday party, do you help choose the present you will take? Shopping for a gift is fun, but finding a present that a friend is sure to like can sometimes be a problem. On the other hand, buying a book for a friend is a great way to give the "perfect" gift.

Does your friend like adventures, science projects, horses, fairy tales, jokes and riddles, or space ships? No matter what a person likes to do or is interested in, there is always a book that's just right.

Another good thing about books is that they don't break or get used up. You can enjoy them again and again. So, the next time you have to buy a present, ask someone to take you to a bookstore. If you have never been to one before, you have a wonderful surprise waiting for you. And who knows, maybe you will find a book you want for your very own!

FULL-LENGTH BOOK

Ox-Cart Man

written by Donald Hall
illustrated by Barbara Cooney

In October he backed his ox into his cart
and he and his family filled it up
with everything they made or grew all year long
that was left over.

He packed a bag of wool
he sheared from the sheep in April.

He packed a shawl his wife wove on a loom
from yarn spun at the spinning wheel
from sheep sheared in April.

He packed five pairs of mittens
his daughter knit
from yarn spun at the spinning wheel
from sheep sheared in April.

He packed candles the family made.

He packed linen made from flax they grew.

He packed shingles he split himself.

He packed birch brooms his son carved
with a borrowed kitchen knife.

He packed potatoes they dug from their garden
–but first he counted out potatoes enough to eat all winter
and potatoes for seed next spring.

He packed a barrel of apples

honey and honeycombs

turnips and cabbages

a wooden box of maple sugar
from the maples they tapped in March

when they boiled and boiled and boiled the sap away.

He packed a bag of goose feathers that his children
collected from the barnyard geese.

When his cart was full, he waved good-bye to his wife, his daughter, and his son

and he walked at his ox's head ten days

over hills, through valleys, by streams

past farms and villages

until he came to Portsmouth
and Portsmouth Market.

He sold the bag of wool.

He sold the shawl his wife made.

He sold five pairs of mittens.

He sold candles and shingles.

He sold birch brooms.

He sold potatoes.

He sold apples.

He sold honey and honeycombs,
turnips and cabbages.

He sold maple sugar.

He sold a bag of goose feathers.

Then he sold the wooden box he carried the maple sugar in.

Then he sold the barrel he carried the apples in.

Then he sold the bag he carried the potatoes in.

Then he sold his ox cart.

Then he sold his ox, and kissed him good-bye on his nose.

Then he sold his ox's yoke and harness.

With his pockets full of coins, he walked through
Portsmouth Market.

He bought an iron kettle to hang over the fire at home,

and for his daughter he bought an embroidery needle
that came from a boat in the harbor
that had sailed all the way from England,

and for his son he bought a Barlow knife,
for carving birch brooms with

and for the whole family he bought two pounds
of wintergreen peppermint candies.

Then he walked home, with the needle and the knife
and the wintergreen peppermint candies tucked into the kettle,

and a stick over his shoulder, stuck through the kettle's handle,
and coins still in his pockets,

past farms and villages,
over hills, through valleys, by streams,

until he came to his farm,
and his son, his daughter, and his wife were waiting for him,

and his daughter took her needle and began stitching,

and his son took his Barlow knife and started whittling,

and they cooked dinner in their new kettle,

and afterward everyone ate a wintergreen peppermint candy,

and that night the ox-cart man sat in front of his fire
stitching new harness
for the young ox in the barn

and he carved a new yoke

and sawed planks for a new cart

and split shingles all winter,

while his wife made flax into linen all winter,

and his daughter embroidered linen all winter,

and his son carved Indian brooms from birch all winter,

and everybody made candles,

and in March they tapped the sugar maple trees

and boiled the sap down,

and in April they sheared the sheep,
spun yarn,
and wove and knitted,

and in May they planted potatoes,
turnips, and cabbages,

while apple blossoms bloomed and fell,

while bees woke up, starting to make
new honey,

and geese squawked in the barnyard,

dropping feathers as soft as clouds.

GLOSSARY

Full pronunciation key* The pronunciation of each word is shown just after the word, in this way: **abbreviate** (ə brē′vē āt).

The letters and signs used are pronounced as in the words below.

The mark **′** is placed after a syllable with primary or heavy accent as in the example above.

The mark ′ after a syllable shows a secondary or lighter accent, as in **abbreviation** (ə brē′vē ā′shən).

SYMBOL	KEY WORDS	SYMBOL	KEY WORDS	SYMBOL	KEY WORDS
a	ask, fat	u	up, cut	r	red, dear
ā	ape, date	ʉr	fur, fern	s	sell, pass
ä	car, father			t	top, hat
		ə	a in ago	v	vat, have
e	elf, ten		e in agent	w	will, always
er	berry, care		e in father	y	yet, yard
ē	even, meet		i in unity	z	zebra, haze
			o in collect		
i	is, hit		u in focus	ch	chin, arch
ir	mirror, here			ng	ring, singer
ī	ice, fire	b	bed, dub	sh	she, dash
		d	did, had	th	thin, truth
o	lot, pond	f	fall, off	*th*	then, father
ō	open, go	g	get, dog	zh	s in pleasure
ô	law, horn	h	he, ahead		
oi	oil, point	j	joy, jump	’	as in (ā′b’l)
o͝o	look, pull	k	kill, bake		
o͞o	ooze, tool	l	let, ball		
yo͝o	unite, cure	m	met, trim		
yo͞o	cute, few	n	not, ton		
ou	out, crowd	p	put, tap		

*Pronunciation key and respellings adapted from *Webster's New World Dictionary, Basic School Edition*, Copyright © 1983 by Simon & Schuster, Inc. Reprinted by permission.

A

ac·cor·di·on (ə kôr′dē ən) a musical instrument with a keyboard and bellows for forcing the air over reeds: "Everyone danced while Rosa played the *accordion.*"

accordion

an·ni·ver·sa·ry (an′ə vûr′sər ē) the date on which something happened in an earlier year: "Carla's parents celebrated their fifteenth wedding *anniversary* yesterday."

a·ris·to·crats (ə ris′tə krats) wealthy people or rulers: "We pretended to be *aristocrats* and drank tea from fancy cups."

ar·ranged (ə rānjd′) **1.** placed in a certain order. **2.** changed so as to fit. **3.** made plans: "We *arranged* to meet after school."

ar·row·head (ar′ō hed′) the pointed tip of an arrow: "Carlos found an *arrowhead* made out of stone."

a·shamed (ə shāmd′) **1.** feeling shame because of something bad or foolish that was done. **2.** not willing because of a fear that one will feel shame or be embarrassed: "I was *ashamed* to ask for Felicia's help."

assembly

as·sem·bly (ə sem′blē) a group of people gathered together: "We sat all the way in the back of the school *assembly.*"

au·thors (ô′thərz) **1.** persons who write books or stories: "The *authors* of these books have written other stories." **2.** persons who make or begin something, creators.

au·to·mo·biles (ôt′ə mə bēlz′ *or* ôt′ə mə bēlz′) vehicles moved by an engine and used to travel on streets or roads: "The teenagers drove their *automobiles* up and down the street."

automobiles

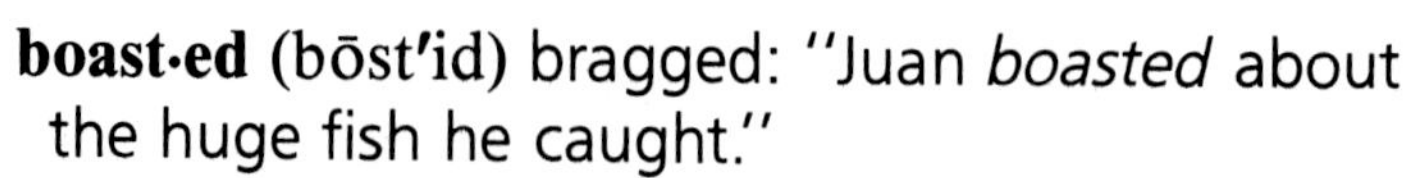

B

bowed

boast·ed (bōst′id) bragged: "Juan *boasted* about the huge fish he caught."

bounced (bo͝onsd) made something spring back by hitting it against a surface: "We *bounced* the ball on the floor."

bowed (bo͝od) bent the head or body downward: "She *bowed* to the audience at the end of the school play."

bris·tling (bris″lin͡g) becoming filled with anger and ready to fight back: "Willie was so angry that he was *bristling*."

bureau

brought (brôt) carried or taken to a place: "Ted *brought* his lunch to school."

bu·reau (byo͝or′ō) **1.** a chest of drawers in which clothes are kept. **2.** of or belonging to such a chest of drawers: "The *bureau* drawers were made from the same kind of wood as the mirror frame."

C

caboose

ca·boose (kə bo͞os′) a car for the crew on a train, usually the last car: "We finally saw the end of the train as the *caboose* rounded the bend."

cap·i·tal (kap′ə t′l) where the government is located: "Our whole class visited Boston, the *capital* of Massachusetts."

cat·tle (kat″l) animals of the cow family such as cows and bulls: "The *cattle* like to eat the grass near the stream."

a fat	**oi** oil	**ch** chin
ā ape	**oo** look	**sh** she
ä car, father	**ōō** tool	**th** thin
e ten	**ou** out	***th*** then
er care	**u** up	**zh** leisure
ē even	**ur** fur	**ng** ring
i hit		
ir here	**ə** = a *in* ago	
ī bite, fire	e *in* agent	
o lot	i *in* unity	
ō go	o *in* collect	
ô law, horn	u *in* focus	

chal·lenge (chal′ənj) **1.** question if something is correct. **2.** ask for a contest: "I *challenge* you to a game of chess." **3.** contest: "I accept the *challenge* to play a game of soccer."

chop·sticks (chop′stiks) a pair of thin pencil-shaped sticks used to eat with in some Asian countries: "He used *chopsticks* to lift the food from the bowl to his mouth."

com·mo·tion (kə mō′shen) noisy rushing about: "There was a great *commotion* on the playground when the bell rang."

con·duc·tor (kən duk′tər) **1.** a person who directs, such as the leader of a band. **2.** the person who collects money and gives out tickets on a train or a streetcar: "We ran quickly as we heard the *conductor* yell 'all aboard!' "

coun·ter (koun′tər) **1.** a person or thing that counts. **2.** a small item for keeping count in a game. **3.** a long table in a store or restaurant for serving customers: "The *counter* in the art store was filled with markers, paints, and crayons."

cous·in (kuz′'n) the son or daughter of a person's aunt or uncle: "My aunt's son is my *cousin*."

cush·ions (koosh′nz) pillows or soft pads used as seats: "We sat on *cushions* on the floor."

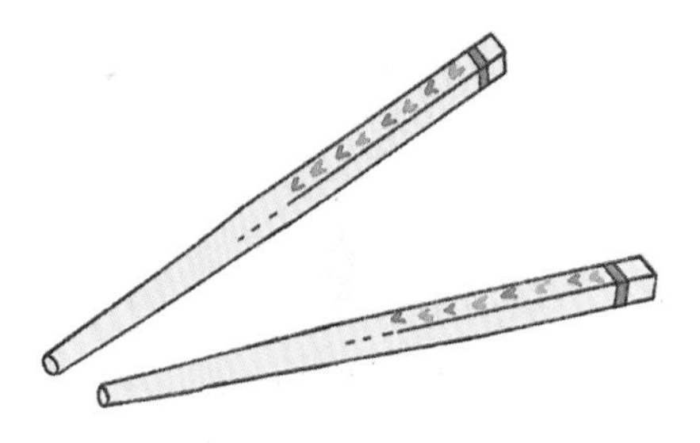

chopsticks

conductor

D

des·ti·na·tions (des′tə nā′shənz) places where people or things will finally arrive: "All of us will visit Disney World, but afterward we have different *destinations*."

diner

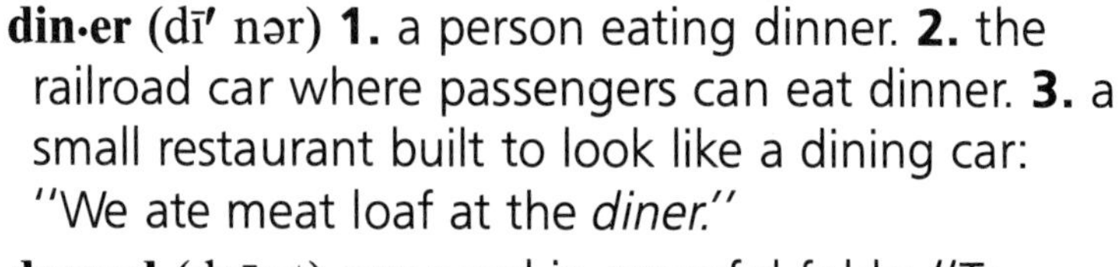

din·er (dī′ nər) **1.** a person eating dinner. **2.** the railroad car where passengers can eat dinner. **3.** a small restaurant built to look like a dining car: "We ate meat loaf at the *diner.*"

draped (drāpt) arranged in graceful folds: "To make his ghost costume, he *draped* a sheet over his head."

drib·bling (drib″ling) in basketball or soccer, the controlling of the ball by using short bounces or short, light kicks: "The team practiced *dribbling* a soccer ball up and down the field."

dribbling

E

emp·ty (emp′tē) having nothing or no one in it: "The jar was *empty.*"

en·gi·neers (en′jə nirz′) **1.** people trained in the field of engineering. **2.** people who drive the engines of trains: "The *engineers* stood on the platform before the trains left for Chicago and Atlanta."

Eng·lish (ing′glish) the main language spoken in such countries as England, the United States, and Australia: "The visitors from France do not speak much *English.*"

engineer

en·ve·lope (en′və lōp *or* on′və lōp) a folded paper cover in which letters are sealed for mailing: "Write the address on the front of the *envelope.*"

e·qual (ē′kwəl) having the same size, number, or value: "Sue and James ate an *equal* number of salty pretzels."

ex·plain (ik splān′ *or* ek splān′) to make clear or plain: "Jim will *explain* how candles are made."

eye·glas·ses (ī′glas iz) lenses fitted into frames to help a person see better:. "John lost his *eyeglasses* at the beach."

a fat	**oi** oil	**ch** chin
ā ape	**oo** look	**sh** she
ä car, father	**ōō** tool	**th** thin
e ten	**ou** out	***th*** then
er care	**u** up	**zh** leisure
ē even	**ur** fur	**ng** ring
i hit		
ir here	ə = a *in* ago	
ī bite, fire	e *in* agent	
o lot	i *in* unity	
ō go	o *in* collect	
ô law, horn	u *in* focus	

F

fe·ro·cious (fə rō′shəs) fierce in a wild way: "The bear's growl sounded *ferocious*."

fid·dle (fid″l) a violin: "He played the *fiddle* while we danced."

flute (flōōt) a musical instrument that makes a high soft sound when you blow into it: "When she played the *flute*, it sounded like birds singing."

frames (frāmz) **1.** the outside part of eyeglasses: "His new glasses have red *frames*." **2.** borders or supports around things, such as pictures, paintings, doors, or windows.

frowned (fround) wrinkled the forehead and drew the eyebrows together when sad, angry, or in deep thought: "Luis *frowned* when he found out the party was canceled."

gerbil

G

ger·bil (jur′b'l) an animal something like a mouse but with longer hind legs: "The pet *gerbil* liked to eat seeds."

goal·ie (gōl′ē) a soccer or hockey player who stays at the goal to keep the ball or puck from entering: "The *goalie* stopped the ball."

goals (gōlz) **1.** scores made in soccer or hockey when the ball or puck passes over the line or goes into the net: "Allison scored two *goals* at the soccer game yesterday." **2.** lines or nets over or into which a ball must go to score.

goalie

H

hauling

haul·ing (hôl′ing) moving something by pulling it: "The children were *hauling* the logs in the little red wagon."

head·board (hed′bôrd) the portion of a bed frame at the head of the bed: "She placed a pillow against the *headboard* so she could sit up and read a book in bed."

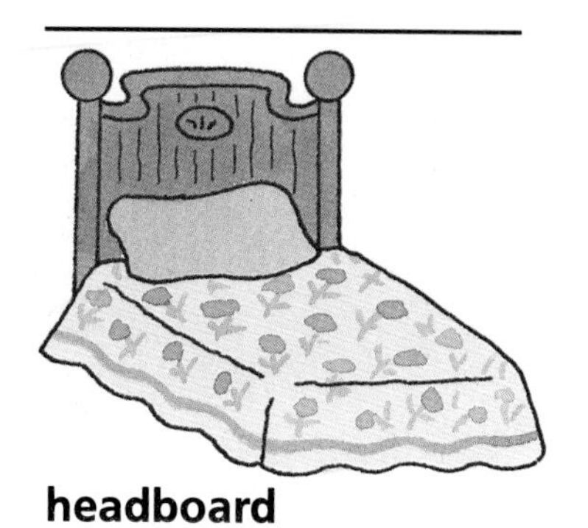

headboard

hon·ors (on′ərz) special praises given for achievements or for high grades: "The best students were given *honors.*"

hop·pers (hop′ərz) **1.** a person or thing that hops. **2.** a container, often shaped like a funnel, from which the contents can be emptied slowly. **3.** railroad cars with funnel-shaped parts: "The *hoppers* were filled to the top with potatoes."

I

instruments

in·stru·ment (in′strə mənt) **1.** a tool for doing exact work. **2.** a device used to make music: "A flute is a musical *instrument.*"

in·ter·views (in′tər vyo͞oz) **1.** meets someone to talk about something, such as a job. **2.** asks a person about their opinions, thoughts, ideas, or activities: "The news reporter often *interviews* people about their opinions and ideas."

a fat	**oi** oil	**ch** chin
ā ape	**oo** look	**sh** she
ä car, father	**ōō** tool	**th** thin
e ten	**ou** out	***th*** then
er care	**u** up	**zh** leisure
ē even	**ur** fur	**ng** ring
i hit		
ir here	**ə** = a *in* ago	
ī bite, fire	e *in* agent	
o lot	i *in* unity	
ō go	o *in* collect	
ô law, horn	u *in* focus	

K

kha·ki (kak′ē) **1.** yellowish brown. **2.** heavy cotton fabric that is yellowish brown: "My dad has washed his *khaki* shirt so many times that it feels soft and smooth."

ki·mo·no (kə mō′nə) a long loose piece of clothing with wide sleeves and a sash: "A *kimono* is worn by some men and women in Japan."

kimonos

L

lan·terns (lan′tərnz) a case of glass or paper holding a light: "The light from the *lanterns* made shadows on the walls."

lens·es (lenz′iz) clear glass or plastic curved so that a person can see better when looking through them: "He could see better when he got new *lenses* in his eyeglasses."

lin·en (lin′ən) **1.** thread or cloth made of flax. **2.** things made from linen or cotton like a tablecloth or sheets. **3.** having to do with these things: "The man on the *linen* truck delivered clean sheets and tablecloths to the hotel."

lo·co·mo·tives (lō′kə mō′tivz) steam, electric, or diesel engines on wheels that pull or push railroad trains: "The *locomotives* parked in the roundhouse for the night."

locomotive

lum·ber (lum′bər) wood that has been sawed into boards: "We like to make boats and houses from scrap *lumber*."

marry

M

mar·ry (mar′ē) to join lives as husband and wife: "My parents wanted to *marry* each other."

mid·night (mid′nīt) twelve o'clock at night, the middle of the night: "At *midnight,* the clock struck twelve."

mon·ey (mun′ē) metal coins or paper bills used in buying and selling: "We paid *money* for it."

mu·sic (myo͞o′zik) songs or melodies: "We like to play *music* together during band practice."

midnight

N

na·tion·al (nash′ə n'l) **1.** of or having to do with the whole country: "The *national* group had people from every part of the country." **2.** of or having to do with people who share the same language or history.

nat·u·ral (nach′ər əl) normal or usual: "It is *natural* for leaves to change their colors in fall."

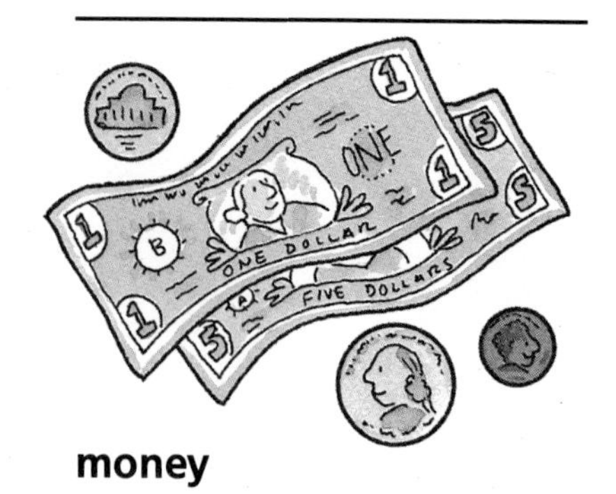

money

O

or·dered (ôr′dərd) **1.** told what to do. **2.** asked for something at a restaurant: "We *ordered* pizza."

out·stand·ing (out stan′diŋ) **1.** that which stands out as very good: "The runner's *outstanding* time set a new record." **2.** not paid yet.

a fat	**oi** oil	**ch** chin
ā ape	**o͝o** look	**sh** she
ä car, father	**o͞o** tool	**th** thin
e ten	**ou** out	***th*** then
er care	**u** up	**zh** leisure
ē even	**ur** fur	**ng** ring
i hit		
ir here	ə = a *in* ago	
ī bite, fire	e *in* agent	
o lot	i *in* unity	
ō go	o *in* collect	
ô law, horn	u *in* focus	

P

pas·sen·gers (pas′'n jərz) persons being carried or driven by car, bus, plane, or train: "There were ten other *passengers* traveling on the train with us."

plat·form (plat′fôrm) a flat surface higher than the floor or ground, for example at a railroad station: "We waited on the *platform* for the train."

R

re·mind (ri mīnd′) to make someone remember or think of something: "Dad asked us to *remind* him to mail the letter."

res·tau·rant (res′tə rənt *or* res′tə ränt) a place to buy and eat meals: "We ate in a *restaurant*."

rhythm (ri*th*′'m) sounds or motions that follow a regular pattern with accents or beats at fixed times: "We danced to the *rhythm* of the music."

passengers

restaurant

S

sci·ence (sī′əns) **1.** knowledge that has been learned through study, observation, experiments, and careful ordering of facts. **2.** having to do with such knowledge: "Our *science* teacher showed us pictures of many kinds of animals and plants."

sci·en·tists (sī′ ən tists) experts in science, such as biologists or chemists: "The *scientists* studied how the plants grew."

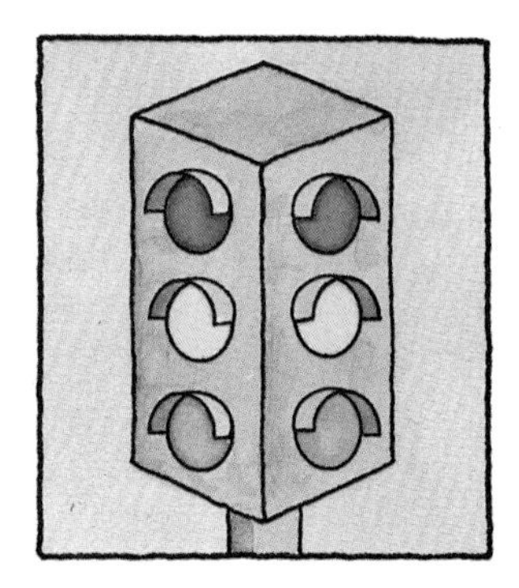

signal

snowflakes

sukiyaki

score (skôr) **1.** the number of points made in a game: "The *score* is 3 to 1." **2.** to win points in a game: "Players *score* points when they kick the ball into the goal."

se·cure (si kyoor′) safe from harm, unafraid: "We found a *secure* spot to hide from the angry bees."

shares (sherz) usually equal parts of something that members of a group get: "Rosa and Tim divided the money equally into two *shares*."

shove (shuv) **1.** to push along a surface. **2.** a strong push: "The *shove* caused Jim to fall."

shrieked (shrēkt) cried out loudly: "Andy *shrieked* in fear when he saw a tree crash into the house."

sig·nal (sig′n′l) a thing used as a warning or a direction: "The red traffic *signal* told us to stop."

snow·flake (snō′flāk) a flake or small piece of snow: "The *snowflake* melted on Bob's nose."

sports (spôrts) games for exercise and fun: "Baseball and swimming are my favorite *sports*."

squint·ed (skwint′əd) looked with eyes partly closed: "She *squinted* as she looked into the sun."

squirmed (skwurmd) wriggled, twisted and turned: "Joe *squirmed* to get away from his sister when she tried to kiss him."

sta·tioned (stā′shənd) placed at a certain station, or post: "She was *stationed* in front of the building."

su·ki·ya·ki (soo′kē yä′kē) a Japanese food made of thinly sliced meat, tofu, and vegetables: "The *sukiyaki* tasted good."

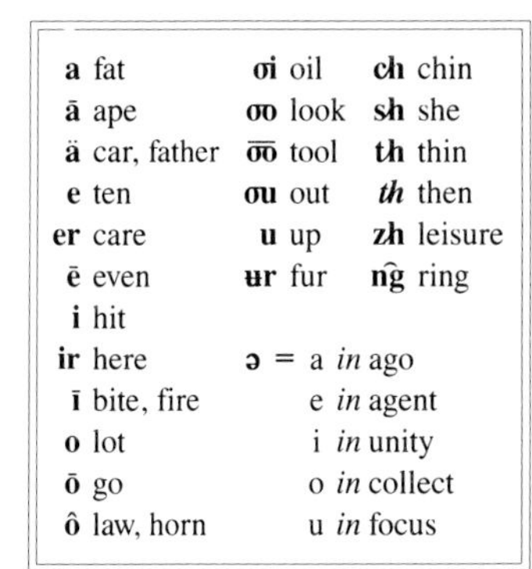

a fat	**oi** oil	**ch** chin
ā ape	**oo** look	**sh** she
ä car, father	**o͞o** tool	**th** thin
e ten	**ou** out	***th*** then
er care	**u** up	**zh** leisure
ē even	**ur** fur	**ng** ring
i hit		
ir here	ə = a *in* ago	
ī bite, fire	e *in* agent	
o lot	i *in* unity	
ō go	o *in* collect	
ô law, horn	u *in* focus	

T

to·fu (tō′fo͞o) a food made from soybeans: "We ate *tofu* for lunch."

U

u·ten·sils (yo͞o ten′s'lz) tools or containers used for special purposes: "Forks are *utensils* for eating."

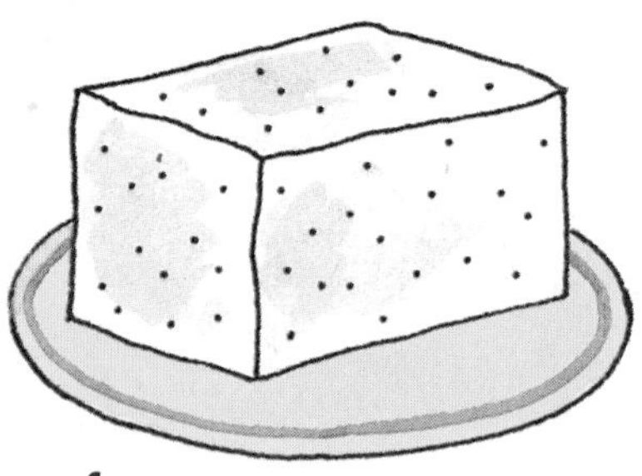

tofu

W

wait·er (wāt′ər) someone who serves people in a restaurant: "The *waiter* brought our food quickly."

Wes·tern (wes′tərn) from Europe or the Americas, the western part of the world: "Some *Western* foods are different from foods eaten in Japan."

wind·shield (wind′shēld) the window in front of the driver's seat of a car: "I had to clear the snow off the *windshield* before I could drive the car."

wip·ers (wī′pərz) two blades that clear a car's windshield of rain or snow: "We watched the *wipers* go back and forth across the windshield of the car."

wrig·gled (rig″ld) twisted and turned from one side to another: "The worm *wriggled* and squirmed when Fred tried to put it on the fishing hook."

waiter

ABOUT THE Authors & Illustrators

JOYCE DURHAM BARRETT

▲ Joyce Durham Barrett and her ten brothers and sisters grew up on a farm in Homer, Georgia. She has fond memories of the paper dolls she made and the doll she once made from a cucumber. There were many chores to do, but there was also time to play in the nearby creek, the hay stacks, and the cotton room. After a long day, her mother would read the comics from the Atlanta paper to the children. That is how she learned to read. Today, Joyce Durham Barrett is a classroom teacher. She enjoys reading to her fifth graders so they can see how powerful stories can be. She says, "My students are a great inspiration to my writing." *Willie's Not the Hugging Kind* is her first book. *(Born 1943)*

PATRICIA REILLY GIFF

✷ Patricia Reilly Giff says she has always loved to read. "I spent most of my childhood with a book in my hands. I read in bed before the sun was up, then hunched over the breakfast table with my book in my lap. After school, I'd sit in the kitchen, leaning against the warm radiator, dreaming over a story." Patricia Reilly Giff says she always wanted to be a writer. She hopes that her books help people realize "that all of us are special . . . important just because we are ourselves." *(Born 1935)*

DONALD HALL

▲ Donald Hall says *Ox-Cart Man* is based on a story that he heard when he was growing up. "I heard the story from my cousin Paul Fenton, my grandfather's nephew. Paul told me *he* had heard it when he was a boy from an old man who told him that he had heard it when he was a boy, from an old man." Donald Hall lives at Eagle Pond Farm where his great-grandfather used to live. *(Born 1928)*

VERA B. WILLIAMS

■ Vera B. Williams has done many things besides being an author and an illustrator. She even helped to start a school for children. The beautiful, rose-covered chair in *Music, Music for Everyone* is the same chair that the girl, her mother, and her grandmother saved for and bought in the book *A Chair for My Mother.* The big chair also has a special meaning for Vera B. Williams. Like the girl's mother who works at the Blue Tile Diner, the author's mother worked hard, too. Vera B. Williams remembers her own mother buying a special chair so that she could have somewhere to rest after work. *(Born 1927)*

MIKE WIMMER

■ Mike Wimmer was born in Oklahoma. As a child he enjoyed art, but what he really wanted to be was a professional football player. When he was young, his father used to bring home eight-foot pieces of cardboard from a box factory. On these, Mike Wimmer drew life-sized pictures of the Incredible Hulk and other super heroes. He used crayons, markers, and sometimes paints. Often he gave the finished pictures to his friends. Now Mike Wimmer likes to paint with oil paints. Frequently his young son works in the studio next to him. *(Born 1961)*

Author Index

Grateful acknowledgment is made to the following publishers, authors, and agents for their permission to reprint copyrighted material. Every effort has been made to locate all copyright proprietors; any errors or omissions in copyright notice are inadvertent and will be corrected in future printings as they are discovered.

Books by Katherine Edelman. Copyright by Katherine Edelman. Used by permission of Katherine Edelman Lyon, Literary Executrix for Katherine Edelman.

Dandelion, story and pictures by Don Freeman. Copyright © 1964 by Don Freeman. Reprinted by permission of Viking Penguin, a division of Penguin Books USA Inc.

The House on Maple Street by Bonnie Pryor, illustrated by Beth Peck. Text copyright © 1987 by Bonnie Pryor, illustrations copyright © 1987 by Beth Peck. Reprinted by permission of William Morrow & Company, Inc./Publishers, New York.

How My Parents Learned to Eat by Ina R. Friedman, illustrated by Allen Say. Text copyright © 1984 by Ina R. Friedman. Illustrations copyright © 1984 by Allen Say. Reprinted by permission of Houghton Mifflin Company. All rights reserved.

"Lee Bennett Hopkins Interviews Bonnie Pryor," © 1993 by Silver Burdett Ginn.

Music, Music for Everyone, written and illustrated by Vera B. Williams, © 1984 by Vera Williams. Reprinted by permission of the American publisher, William Morrow & Company, Inc./Publishers, New York, and of the British publisher, Julia MacRae Books, a division of Walker Books Limited.

Ox-Cart Man by Donald Hall, illustrated by Barbara Cooney. Text Copyright © 1979 by Donald Hall, illustrations Copyright © 1979 by Barbara Cooney Porter. Reprinted by permission of the American publisher, Viking Penguin, a division of Penguin Books USA Inc., and of the British publisher, Julia MacRae Books, a division of Walker Books Limited.

Soccer Sam by Jean Marzollo, illustrated by Blanche Sims. Text Copyright © 1987 by Jean Marzollo. Illustrations Copyright © 1987 by Blanche Sims. Reprinted by permission of Random House, Inc., and of the author and artist's attorney, Sheldon Fogelman.

Train Song by Diane Siebert, illustrated by Mike Wimmer. Text copyright © 1981 by Diane Siebert, illustrations copyright © 1990 by Mike Wimmer. Reprinted by permission of Harper*Collins* Publishers.

Watch Out, Ronald Morgan! by Patricia Reilly Giff with illustrations by Susanna Natti. Text Copyright © 1985 by Patricia Reilly Giff. Illustrations Copyright © 1985 by Susanna Natti. Reprinted by permission of Viking Penguin, a division of Penguin Books USA Inc.

Willie's Not the Hugging Kind by Joyce Durham Barrett. Text copyright © 1989 by Joyce Durham Barrett, illustrations copyright © 1989 by Pat Cummings. Reprinted by permission of Harper*Collins* Publishers.

COVER ILLUSTRATION: Stephen Gammell

ILLUSTRATION: 1-7, Tamar Haber-Schaim; 12-21, Susanna Natti; 22-36, Vera Williams; 38-39, Jennifer Northway; 40-56, Blanche Sims; 57, Susanna Natti; 58-72, Pat Cummings; 73, Cheryl Hanna; 74-97, Don Freeman; 102-120, Mike Wimmer; 121, David Wink; 122-136, Allen Say; 137, Judith Cheng; 138-139, Betsy Day; 144-153, Beth Peck; 155-175, Barbara Cooney; 177, Christine Powers; 178, Diane Dawson Hearn, Christine Powers; 179-180, Christine Powers; 181, Claudia Sargent; 182-186, Christine Powers, Melinda Fabian; 188-190, Tamar Haber-Schaim.

PHOTOGRAPHY: 8-9, SuperStock; 9, THE MARY MCLEOD BETHUNE MEMORIAL, Washington, D.C., bronze statue by Robert Berks, American, ca. 1974. Photo, Paul Conklin; 98-99, © Katrina Thomas/Photo Researchers, Inc.; 99, MEMORIAL WINDOW, by Louis Tiffany, Tiffany Studios, stained glass, American c. 1905. © The Metropolitan Museum of Art, New York, Anonymous Gift in memory of Mr. and Mrs. A. B. Frank, 1981 (1981.159); 100-101, Ken O'Donoghue; 140, provided by Bonnie Pryor; 143, John Moran/Gainsville Sun Photo; 180, SuperStock; 181, Richard Kolar/Animals, Animals; 188, courtesy, Harper*Collins* Publishers; 189, (t) by Karl Bissinger, courtesy, William Morrow & Co., (b) Viking Penguin Inc.; 190, (t) Viking Penguin Inc., (b) courtesy, Harper*Collins* Publishers.